To Matthew

God Bless

Monty   Sept 2010

© Day One Publications 2010
First printed 2010

ISBN 978–1–84625–205–1

British Library Cataloguing in Publication Data available

Published by Day One Publications
Ryelands Road, Leominster, HR6 8NZ
☎ 01568 613 740 FAX 01568 611 473
email—sales@dayone.co.uk
web site—www.dayone.co.uk
North American—e-mail—sales@dayonebookstore.com
North American—web site—www.dayonebookstore.com

Cover design by Wayne McMaster
Printed by Orchard Press, Cheltenham Ltd.

Dr Monty White's critique of the idea of theistic evolution is so thorough and devastating that anyone who reads it and still clings to the position of theistic evolution does so in willing contradiction to biblical teaching.

Dr Duane Gish, former Senior Vice-President, Institute of Creation Research

What About Origins? *is a book designed to challenge those who think there is little, if any, evidence for the biblical account of creation, and to encourage those who just want supporting facts about creation and a way to share it with their friends. Dr Monty White both accepts and defends biblical creation unashamedly and will challenge you to do so too, as well as equip you to expose evolutionist error.*

John Mackay, International Director, Creation Research

This book gives an excellent up-to-date summary of the key arguments for biblical creation. I particularly like the chapter on the origin of life (abiogenesis), which I think is one of the biggest challenges to the theory of evolution.

Professor Stuart Burgess, Bristol University, UK

When the first edition of What About Origins? *was published, there were very few books which promoted the biblical view of origins. Today there are many, yet this revised and updated edition is a welcome addition to the range now available. Monty begins with Scripture, making God's Word the ultimate authority on origins issues. Those who have heard Monty speak will find that he writes in a similarly entertaining and easy-to-understand manner, and I recommend this revised updated edition of* What About Origins? *as a good, up-to-date guide to biblical creationism.*

Geoff Chapman, Director, Creation Resources Trust

I believe that the greatest challenge to Christians today is establishing the truth about our origins, and that arriving at the correct conclusion is absolutely foundational to our faith in God. Long before I produced my first television programme and before launching Revelation TV, I saw the necessity of dealing head-on with three main topics, one of which is presenting sound scientific evidence that supports the biblical account

Commendations

of creation as recorded in Genesis. Today, Christians receive greater criticism and challenges to their faith in God and his Word than ever before, hence the need for them to be equipped with facts and information that can easily be assimilated and passed on to others. This is why I am delighted to recommend Dr Monty White's book What About Origins? for it truly is a comprehensive educational work which gives the evidence and information that supports what the Bible teaches about origins.

Howard Conder, Christian broadcaster,
and founder of Revelation and Genesis TV

This book is dedicated to the

Lord God, who has shown

unto me His mighty and

mysterious and glorious works.

... it is axiomatic that if we are in error about the origins of things, whether of the universe, or life, or religion, or salvation, we shall be in error about all that follows. That is why the questions ... [of origins] ... are of crucial importance for the Christian no less than for mankind in general.

Philip Edgcumbe Hughes, *Christianity and the Problem of Origins*

Contents

FOREWORD TO THE FIRST EDITION **10**

FOREWORD TO THE SECOND EDITION **11**

ABOUT THE AUTHOR **13**

PREFACE **15**

1 THE CREATOR AND HIS WAYS **19**

Scriptural references to the creation **20**

Faith and creation **24**

The sovereignty of God in creation **29**

The fall and restoration of the creation **32**

Conclusion **38**

2 THEISTIC EVOLUTION? **40**

Is Genesis mythical or symbolic? **42**

Is Genesis evolutionary? **47**

Who was Adam? **54**

The biblical view of origins **59**

Conclusion **63**

3 MIND THE GAP! **65**

What does the Gap Theory teach? **66**

Problems with the Gap Theory **67**

Does the Hebrew teach the Gap Theory? **70**

Conclusion **72**

4 THE AGE OF THE EARTH: BIBLICAL CONSIDERATIONS **73**

Contents

Did God create everything in 4004 BC? **73**

Determining the age of the earth from the Bible **74**

Are there gaps in biblical genealogies? **75**

Superficial appearance of age **77**

Conclusion **81**

5 SCIENTIFIC DATING METHODS **83**

How are rocks dated? **84**

Radiometric dating **86**

Radiocarbon dating **94**

Tree-ring dating **100**

Scientific evidence for a young earth **102**

Conclusion **106**

6 THE ORIGIN OF THE UNIVERSE **110**

The nature of the universe **111**

The Big Bang **114**

Problems with the Big Bang **120**

One or many universes? **125**

The understandableness of the universe **126**

The Goldilocks effect **130**

Conclusion **132**

7 THE ORIGIN OF LIFE **136**

No intelligence necessary? **137**

Contents

The earth's atmosphere **139**

A dry soup? **142**

Origin of life and probability **143**

Is God left-handed? **145**

Monkeys and typewriters **148**

Junk yards and jumbo jets **151**

Conclusion **153**

8 THE ORIGIN OF SPECIES **156**

Darwin, species and kinds **157**

Natural selection and evolution **161**

Fossils and evolution **166**

Dinosaurs, birds and evolution **172**

Conclusion **177**

9 THE ORIGIN OF HUMANS **181**

Past mistakes and frauds **182**

Recent mistakes and frauds **187**

Australopithecines—fossil apes **191**

Humankind, past and present **197**

Atheism and evolution **200**

Conclusion **204**

10 GENERAL CONCLUSION **208**

I n this book, *What About Origins?*, Dr White has combined his command of the Scriptures with his scientific training and experience to show the true relationship between the biblical doctrine of creation and the scientific evidence related to origins. His critique of the idea of theistic evolution is so thorough and devastating that anyone who reads it and still clings to the position of theistic evolution does so in willing contradiction to biblical teaching. Dr White also exposes the fallacies inherent in the Gap Theory.

Dr White's analysis of the scientific evidence from the fields of cosmology, biochemistry, geochronology, biology, and palaeontology exposes fallacies and weaknesses in evolution theory and demonstrates the superiority of direct special creation as an explanation for the origin of the universe and of the living things it contains. All who love and honour the Bible as the Word of God, and are interested in the relationship of God's written Word to the revelation he has given us in nature, will enjoy and profit from reading this book, and its reading can provide an interesting and challenging experience to all others.

Dr Duane T. Gish
Institute for Creation Research
1978

In today's scientific world, the critics of biblical creation commonly claim that there are no real scientists who believe that the world or life was created. With a Ph.D. in Chemistry for his research in the field of gas kinetics, combined with his roles on the university campus over many years, Dr Monty White is a living disproof of such criticism.

On TV, and in schools, universities and churches, Monty has for decades consistently spoken out against the errors of Darwinian evolution and publicly defended and promoted both Creator and creation against Darwin's present-day followers.

Darwin's great-grandson Richard Keynes wrote in 2002 about the tragic death of Darwin's favourite daughter, Annie, which profoundly influenced Charles Darwin and motivated him to publicly author *On the Origin of Species*. Keynes stated, 'After Annie's death [in 1851], Charles [Darwin] set the Christian faith firmly behind him … Freed from the last vestige of belief that the world was perfect because God created it that way, Darwin continued without spiritual restraint to work out his theory on the origin of species.'[1]

Most present-day evolutionists fail to remember that Darwin never lived long enough to observe anything evolve, knew nothing about genetics or mutations, and was the first to admit in his chapter on Geology in *On the Origin of Species* that the fossils didn't help his case at all. Darwin never proved evolution, he simply presupposed it and argued from there, emotionally motivated by an anger which caused him to reject God and substitute death and suffering as the norm and the way by which all life evolved.

Charles Darwin graduated from the University of Cambridge with an MA in Theology and he knew exactly what he was seeking to disprove—the first eleven chapters of Genesis. Every Christian does need to know how and why Darwin's work has so radically affected Christianity and how to share the facts of creation and the Creator Jesus Christ with those who think that evolution is a fact and who consequently believe that the Word of God from Genesis to Revelation can be ignored. Monty White's book helps us where the rubber hits the road. As the world has been celebrating the 200th anniversary of Charles Darwin's birth and the 150th anniversary of the publication of *On the Origin of Species*, this new updated edition of *What About Origins?* will prove a great help to both scientist and layperson alike.

After I graduated in Geology, one big difficulty I faced was the evidence for the billions-of-years age of the earth. You will be as greatly helped by this new expanded and updated edition as I was when I first read the well-summarized evidence in Monty's first edition. The evidence does not show that the world has had billions of years to evolve, and there is much data supportive of and consistent with the biblical picture of six-day creation. The dating section proved to be my favourite in the original, and I have won not a few debates because of the accuracy of the information it contains.

What About Origins? is a book designed to challenge those who think there is little, if any, evidence for the biblical account of creation, and to encourage those who simply want supporting facts about creation and a way to share it with their friends. Dr Monty White both accepts and defends biblical creation unashamedly and will challenge you to do the same, as well as equip you to expose evolutionist error.

I am personally very happy to commend this book to everyone because Monty doesn't just talk about the Bible and Jesus Christ being true; he shows it in the life choices he makes and shares publicly.

John Mackay
International Director of Creation Research
2010

Notes

1 Quoted in *Science*, 296/5575 (14 June 2002), p. 1974.

D r A. J. Monty White was converted to Christianity from atheism in 1964, when he was an undergraduate student at the University College of Wales, Aberystwyth. While reading for an honours degree in Chemistry, he also studied Geology, which led to his belief in theistic evolution—that evolution had occurred, but God had controlled the processes. He thought that this was the only way he could reconcile evolution with Scripture. In 1969 he undertook a study of the Scriptures and also of the scientific 'evidence' proffered as proof of evolution. After two years he came to the conclusion that 'in six days the Lord made the heavens and the earth, the sea, and all that is in them' (Exod. 20:11). His first book, *What About Origins?*, was written as a result of this study.

Monty obtained his B.Sc. in 1967 and was awarded a Ph.D. in 1970 for his research in the field of Gas Kinetics. After a further two years of chemical research at Aberystwyth, Monty moved to Cardiff, where he held a number of senior administrative posts at Cardiff University until September 2000, when he became Chief Executive of Answers in Genesis (UK/Europe), which has its headquarters in Leicester. After leaving Answers in Genesis in July 2008, Monty set up Biblical Foundations; since then he has had an itinerant ministry, speaking and preaching, with his wife, Irene.

Monty has written four books and has had hundreds of articles and pamphlets dealing with the subject of creation and evolution published worldwide. His writings have been translated into French, Dutch, German, Portuguese and Swedish. Monty has spoken and lectured extensively in the UK and throughout Europe, as well as in Hong Kong and the USA. From 1983 until 2001, Monty was a guest lecturer on the subject of 'The Bible and Science' at the State Independent Theological University of Basel, Switzerland.

Although Monty has retained his interest in Chemistry and is a Chartered Chemist and a Member of the Royal Society of Chemistry, he has also continued his love of Geology and, together with his wife, spends much of his spare time studying geological formations in the field and searching for fossils.

Monty has three grown-up children and one grandson.

When I first wrote *What About Origins?* there were very few resources propagating creationist views. I had begun to speak publicly about the biblical view of origins and I was producing a bi-monthly newsletter (*Creation News Sheet*) that had a circulation of several thousand. More and more people were asking me to write something substantial about origins and so I put pen to paper (literally, as there were no PCs at the time!). The result was *What About Origins?* I approached a number of publishers, but they were not interested as I was an unknown, and they maintained that no one was interested in the subject of origins. Christian friends were praying that I would get my manuscript published and, one day, a good friend, Brian Grantham-Hill, telephoned me to say that he knew a printer who was looking for this type of material to publish. This resulted in my meeting Thomas Daniel, who at that time owned Dunestone Printers, a small printing business in Kingsteignton in Devon.

Thomas said that he would only publish my manuscript if I could get a well-known creationist such as Dr Duane Gish to write the Foreword. A few weeks later, the late David C. C. Watson, who had recently had his creationist book *The Great Brain Robbery* published, contacted me to say that Dr Duane Gish was in the UK and that he wanted to meet me. David brought Duane to Cardiff, where I asked him if he would read my manuscript and do me the honour of writing the Foreword. A few weeks later, I received a very supportive Foreword from Duane and, as result, *What About Origins?* was published by Dunestone Printers in 1978.

The origins of the universe, of the earth, of life, of species and of humans are questions that have taxed the minds of scientists and philosophers for centuries. Who or what is responsible for all the things that we see around us? *Is* anyone or anything responsible? Where did everything come from? How? When? Why? These are some of the questions for which answers have long been sought. Many hypotheses, explanations and ideas have been put forward to try to explain the existence of the cosmos, yet the ultimate answers to the questions of origins are only to be found in the Bible. It is in this book, and in this book alone, that we discover the answer, not only to the question of who is responsible, but also concerning the methods employed, when everything originated and also, importantly, why everything originated.

Preface

The intent of *What About Origins?* is to examine exactly what the Bible teaches about origins. The reasons for this are many and varied, but principally twofold. Firstly, there can be no compromise between the evolutionary views of scientists and the biblical account of origins. Secondly, the majority of people have been brainwashed by education systems and the media into believing that evolution is a proven fact when this is manifestly not so.

Christians may take issue with me for writing on the subject of origins. Some argue, for example, that the message of the gospel—'For God so loved the world that He gave His only begotten Son, that whoever believes in Him should not perish but have everlasting life' (John 3:16)—is *the* vital message for *every* individual and that the question of origins is of low priority. Some may ask, 'Why waste time fighting on the creation/evolution battlefront when there are far more important issues in which to be involved?' Some argue that the creation/evolution question has been settled by the scientists and they have proved evolution to be a fact, so why take issue with them? Others may wonder whether it really matters if we believe that the Genesis account of the creation and early history of the earth is historically accurate; surely, as long as we believe that God was in control of the processes, that is all that needs to concern us?

A Christian's beliefs concerning the Genesis account of creation are, however, important, in that they indicate that person's attitude towards the authority of the Word of God—not only for the book of Genesis, but also for other books of the Bible, especially the ones that explicitly explain the way of salvation. Ultimately, the biblical view of origins boils down to the question: Creation or evolution? Now, this question is basically a question about authority—the authority of God versus the authority of scientists; the authority of the Word of God versus the authority of the words of scientists; the authority of the Bible versus the authority of scientific textbooks. It also needs to be pointed out that the gospel message does not make sense unless a historical Christ died because a historical Adam sinned.

The contents of this book are based on the assumption that the Bible is the infallible and totally inspired Word of God: 'All Scripture is given by inspiration of God, and is profitable for doctrine, for reproof, for correction, for instruction in righteousness, that the man of God may be complete, thoroughly equipped for every good work' (2 Tim. 3:16–17).

I have no intention of defending Scripture—the Bible fights its own battles: 'For the word of God is living and powerful, and sharper than any two-edged sword, piercing even to the division of soul and spirit, and of joints and marrow, and is a discerner of the thoughts and intents of the heart' (Heb. 4:12). Because this is my presupposition, I have quoted Scripture liberally throughout this book, believing that the Bible does not merely contain some truth, but it records *the truth*.

Readers will find that most of the time I quote from the New King James Version of the Bible, although I sometimes quote from other versions too. I also refer to the original Hebrew or Greek words used when it is expedient to get a clearer or deeper meaning of the text, so that our understanding of the Word of God may be enhanced.

I have endeavoured to write with the average Christian layperson (if such an individual exists!) in mind. Hence I have tried to keep the science content both minimal and as simple as possible. This, however, has been very difficult to do at times because of the very topics that are being discussed. I trust that the reader will bear with me on these occasions and will try to follow the arguments that I use.

I know that the first edition of this book was a great help and blessing to many people. I have been amazed at the number of people who have written to me or come up to me and told me how, as a result of reading *What About Origins?*, they became Christians or started to take the early chapters of the Bible literally. More recently, people have asked me to rewrite *What About Origins?*, bringing the science up to date and adding new material that I have come across over the years. This second edition is the result of such requests. My prayer is that this edition will be used by the Lord to bring even more people to a saving knowledge of him.

Finally, I trust that, while reading this book, the reader will be constantly reminded of the words of the apostle Paul:

But God has chosen the foolish things of the world to put to shame the wise, and God has chosen the weak things of the world to put to shame the things which are mighty; and the base [or 'insignificant' or 'lowly'] things of the world and the things which are despised God has chosen, and the things which are not, to bring to nothing the things that are, that no flesh should glory in His presence. (1 Cor. 1:27–29)

Dr A. J. Monty White
2010

The Creator and his ways

There is no Introduction, Preface or Foreword to the Genesis account of the creation. Without hesitation or apology, Genesis 1 records that *God* is the Creator of everything and that he created everything in *six days*. That this is so is also stated clearly in the middle of the fourth commandment: 'For in six days the LORD made the heavens and the earth, the sea, and all that is in them, and rested the seventh day' (Exod. 20:11).

Some people argue that the days in Genesis 1 are not literal days. However, the Hebrew word that is translated 'day' in that chapter is *yom*. In the context in which it is used throughout the chapter, this word *yom* means—and can only mean—a literal day. This can be shown by studying the use and meaning of the word *yom* elsewhere in the Old Testament. Whenever the word *yom* is found outside of Genesis 1 with a numeral (one, two, three, four and so on)—and this occurs 410 times in the singular and plural—it always means a literal day. Furthermore, whenever the word *yom* is found outside of Genesis 1 together with the phrase 'evening and morning'—and this occurs no fewer than thirty-eight times—it always means a literal day. Finally, whenever the word *yom* is found outside of Genesis 1 with either the word 'evening' or the word 'morning'—and this occurs twenty-three times with each one—it always means a literal day. From these textual considerations it can be seen that the days in Genesis 1 can only be literal days.

Genesis 1 also provokes the question: Who made God? Again, we have to turn to the Bible to find the answer to this question, for it is in this book, and in this book alone, that we learn about God. The Bible is the Word of God rather than the thoughts and ideas of any human being, and it is the only book that tells us about God—the one true God, the Creator of everything. When we search the Scriptures we learn that God did not have a beginning—he has always existed—and it follows that he did not have a creator—no one made him! To ask the question 'Who made God?' is to ask nonsense along the lines of 'What does the colour red smell like?' The colour red does not have a smell. God did not have a beginning; God did not have a creator—he has always been and always will be. There never was a time when God was not. This may be hard for us to understand fully, but it is a fundamental truth taught by Scripture.

In the Genesis account of the creation, we are confronted, not with man, but with God. Here at the very beginning we meet God; here from the very beginning we are introduced to the Bible's approach to all things: everything is seen, not only from God's point of view, but also with God as pre-eminent. Here, I believe, is a lesson for us all: many of our problems and difficulties stem from the tendency to look at things from our point of view—we look at ourselves with our changeableness and weaknesses instead of looking at God's unchanging sovereignty and glorious power.

This is one of the failings of the Christian church today—she has lost her vision of the true nature of God and has become too man-centred. Hence *theology*, which simply means 'the truth about God', is seen to be academic, dull, boring and irrelevant, whereas it is really the only possible foundation of a Christian life. By losing their vision of the mighty power of God, many Christians have rejected God as the Creator of all things. Instead of looking to God and his infallible Word, the Bible, they have instead looked to fallible man (to scientists, in particular) to furnish the answers to the questions about origins. To such Christians I would plead that they turn their eyes back to God and to his infallible Word rather than look to scientists and their ever-changing ideas, discoveries and textbooks.

Scriptural references to the creation

Scriptural references to the doctrine of creation by Almighty God are not confined to the first chapter of the book of Genesis, but are found throughout the whole of the Bible. It will be profitable for us to look at some of the passages of Scripture that refer to creation in order to comprehend the great extent to which this doctrine permeates the pages of the Word of God and is relevant to Christians living in the twenty-first century. It should be remembered that the following references are by no means exhaustive.

HISTORICAL BOOKS

Part of the prayer of the Levites:

You alone are the LORD;
You have made heaven,
The heaven of heavens, with all their host,
The earth and everything on it,
The seas and all that is in them,
And You preserve them all.
The host of heaven worships You.   (Neh. 9:6)

THE LAW

The fourth commandment:

Remember the Sabbath day, to keep it holy. Six days you shall labor and do all your work, but the seventh day is the Sabbath of the LORD your God. In it you shall do no work: you, nor your son, nor your daughter, nor your male servant, nor your female servant, nor your cattle, nor your stranger who is within your gates. For in six days the LORD made the heavens and the earth, the sea, and all that is in them, and rested the seventh day. Therefore the LORD blessed the Sabbath day and hallowed it.

(Exod. 20:8–11)

Moses speaking to the Israelites:

For ask now concerning the days that are past, which were before you, since the day that God created man on the earth, and ask from one end of heaven to the other, whether any great thing like this has happened, or anything like it has been heard. Did any people ever hear the voice of God speaking out of the midst of the fire, as you have heard, and live?   (Deut. 4:32–33)

THE BOOKS OF WISDOM

Then the LORD answered Job out of the whirlwind, and said:
'Who is this who darkens counsel
By words without knowledge?
Now prepare yourself like a man;

Chapter 1

I will question you, and you shall answer Me.
Where were you when I laid the foundations of the earth?
Tell Me, if you have understanding.
Who determined its measurements?
Surely you know!
Or who stretched the line upon it?
To what were its foundations fastened?
Or who laid its cornerstone,
When the morning stars sang together,
And all the sons of God shouted for joy?
Or who shut in the sea with doors,
When it burst forth and issued from the womb;
When I made the clouds its garment,
And thick darkness its swaddling band;
When I fixed My limit for it,
And set bars and doors;
When I said,
"This far you may come, but no farther,
And here your proud waves must stop!"'   (Job 38:1–11)

By the word of the LORD the heavens were made,
And all the host of them by the breath of His mouth.
He gathers the waters of the sea together as a heap;
He lays up the deep in storehouses.

(Ps. 33:6–7; see also 102:25; 121:2; 124:8; 136:5–9; 146:5–6; 148:1–5)

The hearing ear and the seeing eye,
The LORD has made them both.   (Prov. 20:12)

THE PROPHETS

For thus says the LORD,
Who created the heavens,
Who is God,
Who formed the earth and made it,
Who has established it,

Who did not create it in vain,
Who formed it to be inhabited:
'I am the LORD, and there is no other.'   (Isa. 45:18)

He has made the earth by His power,
He has established the world by His wisdom,
And has stretched out the heavens at His discretion.
      (Jer. 10:12; see also Isa. 37:16; 40:12, 21–22, 26; 44:24; 48:13; 51:13, 16; Jer. 51:15)

THE GOSPELS

Jesus speaking to his disciples:

For in those days there will be tribulation, such as has not been since the beginning of
the creation which God created until this time, nor ever shall be.
                  (Mark 13:19; see also Matt. 19:3–6; Mark 10:2–9; John 1:3, 10)

THE EPISTLES

Therefore, just as through one man sin entered the world, and death through sin, and
thus death spread to all men, because all sinned—(For until the law sin was in the
world, but sin is not imputed when there is no law. Nevertheless death reigned from
Adam to Moses, even over those who had not sinned according to the likeness of the
transgression of Adam, who is a type of Him who was to come …)   (Rom. 5:12–14)

For man is not from woman, but woman from man. Nor was man created for the
woman, but woman for the man.   (1 Cor. 11:8–9)

For as in Adam all die, even so in Christ all shall be made alive.   (1 Cor. 15:22)

To me, who am less than the least of all the saints, this grace was given, that I should
preach among the Gentiles the unsearchable riches of Christ, and to make all see what
is the fellowship of the mystery, which from the beginning of the ages has been hidden
in God who created all things through Jesus Christ …   (Eph. 3:8–9)

For Adam was formed first, then Eve.   (1 Tim. 2:13)

God, who at various times and in various ways spoke in time past to the fathers by the prophets, has in these last days spoken to us by His Son, whom He has appointed heir of all things, through whom also He made the worlds.　　　　　　　　(Heb. 1:1–2)

THE BOOK OF REVELATION

The twenty-four elders around the throne of God:

You are worthy, O Lord,
To receive glory and honor and power;
For You created all things,
And by Your will they exist and were created.　　　　　　　　(Rev. 4:11)

A flying angel:

Fear God and give glory to Him, for the hour of His judgment has come; and worship Him who made heaven and earth, the sea and springs of water.　　　　　　　(Rev. 14:7)

Faith and creation

It is plain from the above Scriptures that creation by Almighty God is an indisputable teaching of the Word of God. Ultimately, however, biblical truth, including the doctrine of creation, can only be understood by *faith*. Now this is not that faith described by Mark Twain when he said that 'Faith is believing what you know ain't so',[1] but it is that true biblical faith defined by the writer of the book of Hebrews as 'the substance of things hoped for, the evidence of things not seen' (Heb. 11:1). True faith is based not on empirical evidence, but on divine assurance.

The essence of the doctrine of creation is also found in the book of Hebrews, for we read in Hebrews 11:3, 'By faith we understand that the worlds were framed by the word of God, so that the things which are seen were not made of things which are visible.' Although in Romans 1:20 the Bible teaches clearly that the invisible nature of the Godhead may be plainly understood by the things which are seen (that is, the visible creation), the Bible also teaches that people's understanding has been darkened and their eyes blinded by the god of this world (see Eph. 4:18; 2 Cor. 4:4). The truth about creation, therefore, is outside the realm of the understanding of the non-Christian apart from by spiritual revelation: 'But the natural man does not receive the things of the Spirit of God, for they are foolishness to him; nor can he know them, because they are spiritually discerned' (1 Cor. 2:14). Hence only the Christian can really understand and appreciate fully the doctrine of supernatural creation.

One of the problems we have in appreciating creation is that there is no analogy in modern human experience to define and fully comprehend it. The word that is used in Genesis 1 to convey that God created all things is the Hebrew word *barah*. This word is translated 'created', but Dr John Whitcomb gives its fuller meaning as 'a sudden supernatural bringing into existence of highly complex things by the mere spoken word of an omnipotent God'.[2] He goes on to point out that *barah* never means 'long-drawn-out, merely providential, trial-and-error processes' but that it always means 'supernatural, sudden creation'. This is something that is clearly taught in Scripture.

Christians therefore believe in an *ex nihilo* (literally, 'out of nothing') creation because of their faith. It is not by observation, it is not by experimentation, it is not by scientific method, it is not because of the modern discoveries of science that lend support to the biblical account of the creation and the early history of the earth, but it is by faith. Now this faith is not just a mental assent to, or an acknowledgement of, Christian 'ideology', but it is a living, supernatural faith born of revelation; it is an embracing of, and a commitment to, the authority of the Word of the Author of that revelation; it is the acceptance of the authority of the living God; it is to take God at his word. In 1 Corinthians 14:33 we read that God is not the author of confusion; neither is he a confused author! Any confusion arising in people's minds when they read and study the Bible is often of their own making or due to lack of understanding. The only way to understand the Bible is to take a *literal* and *logical* approach to it, while at the same time asking the Holy Spirit for his help to enable us to comprehend it.

Evolutionists likewise believe in evolution because of their faith rather than because of any evidence that they may have to prove it. Again, it is not by observation, experimentation, scientific method, nor because of the modern discoveries of science, but it is by faith—faith in extrapolation, in natural processes operating over vast periods of time, in speculation and in missing links.

Evolutionists' faith in extrapolation can be demonstrated by considering their belief that 'the present is the key to the past'. This idea proposes that observed processes (especially geological ones) in the present determine what has happened in the past. This was first suggested by Scottish naturalists (David Hume and James Hutton being the most notable) towards the end of the eighteenth century and, after refinement by John Playfair, it was popularized by Charles Lyell in his *magnum opus*, *Principles of Geology*, in 1830. A careful examination of this idea actually illustrates that what evolutionists do is to observe the present and then extrapolate (or guess) what happened in the past. Mark Twain demonstrates the absurdities of extrapolation in the following illustration:

In the space of one hundred and seventy-six years the Lower Mississippi has shortened itself two hundred and forty-two miles. That is an average of a trifle over one mile and a third per year. Therefore, any calm person, who is not blind or idiotic, can see that in the Old Oolitic Silurian Period, just a million years ago … the Lower Mississippi River was upward of one million three hundred thousand miles long, and stuck out over the Gulf of Mexico like a fishing-rod.[3]

He then goes on to show the absurdities of extrapolating into the future, continuing, 'And by the same token any person can see that seven hundred and forty-two years from now the Lower Mississippi will be only a mile and three-quarters long, and Cairo and New Orleans will have joined their streets together, and be plodding comfortably along under a single mayor and a mutual board of aldermen.' Finally, Mark Twain cynically remarks that 'There is something fascinating about science. One gets such wholesale returns of conjecture out of such a trifling investment of fact.'[4]

The evolutionist's faith in natural processes to produce not only life but also intelligence and design is demonstrated by Professor Richard Dawkins, who was reported as saying,

I believe that all life, all intelligence, all creativity and all 'design' anywhere in the universe is the direct or indirect product of Darwinian natural selection. It follows that design comes late in the universe, after a period of Darwinian evolution. Design cannot precede evolution and therefore cannot underlie the universe.[5]

But what Richard Dawkins is actually doing is assuming that evolution has taken place and that, as a result, it has produced what he refers to as 'design'. He then concludes that design cannot come before evolution. Yet he assumed in the first place that evolution produced 'design' in order to prove that design came after evolution! This is not science—it is speculation based on Dawkins' belief system.

Furthermore, that evolution is speculation and that it has not been subjected to scientific method is aptly illustrated by the following quote from Edwin G. Conklin, a former Professor of Biology at Princeton University: 'The concept of organic evolution is very highly prized by biologists, for many of whom it is an object of genuinely religious devotion, because they regard it as a supreme integrative principle. This is probably the reason why severe methodological criticism employed in other departments of biology has not yet been brought to bear on evolutionary speculation.'[6]

Evolutionists also believe that natural processes operating *over eons* have been responsible for producing all the life forms that are alive on our planet today, as well as those that we find fossilized in the sedimentary rocks. Charles Darwin was fully aware of the time factor when he wrote in *On the Origin of Species* that anyone who 'does not admit how incomprehensibly vast have been the past periods of time may at once close this volume'.[7] It seems that the enormous time periods that are proposed by evolutionists (4,600 million years for the age of the earth, for example) deaden the mind and cause people to believe the unbelievable—'goo-to-you-via-the-zoo', as a comical definition of evolution puts it. The faith that evolutionists have in natural processes operating over vast periods of time has been formulated by Dr John Whitcomb into the Evolutionists' Version of Hebrews 11:3: 'By faith, we evolutionists understand that the worlds were framed not by the word of any personal God, but were brought into existence through endless ages of time by purely natural processes, from simple to complex, without any miracles at all, so that things which are seen were indeed made of previously existing, visible, simpler, physical entities.'[8]

Later, we will be considering the non-existence of transitional forms (the so-called 'missing links') in the fossil record. At this point, however, it is worth revealing that in a letter to the prestigious journal *Science* in 1973, E. C. Lucas pointed out that 'evolutionists have to have faith in the original existence of the missing transitional forms'.[9] And so they do! The evolutionists' faith could be defined as *the fossils hoped for, the evidence of missing links not seen.*

It is worth noting that it is not just creationists who talk about the evolutionists' faith—so, too, do the evolutionists themselves! The late L. T. More, who was Professor of Physics at the University of Cincinnati, penned the following remarkable confession: 'Our *faith* in the idea of evolution depends upon our reluctance to accept the antagonistic doctrine of special creation' (emphasis added).[10]

Evolutionists therefore prefer to have faith in extrapolation, natural processes operating over vast periods of time, speculation, and missing links, rather in the God of the Bible. Given evolution's need for faith, it has, naturally enough, many of the characteristics of a religion.[11] The evolutionists' belief in evolution, whether they realize it or not, affects their whole way of life—their unbelief in a personal God who is the Creator of the heavens and the earth; their unbelief in the Bible as the authoritative Word of God; their unbelief in Jesus Christ, the Son of the living God; their unbelief in salvation by the atoning death of Jesus Christ on the cross of Calvary; their unbelief in a duty towards God and their fellow humans; their unbelief in an absolute moral code of conduct; and so on. Interestingly, in response to the question 'Is atheism the logical extension of believing evolution?', the famous atheistic evolutionist Richard Dawkins replied, 'My personal feeling is that understanding evolution led me to atheism.'[12] Furthermore, the plain fact that, if you do not believe in evolution you are treated as a heretic by evolutionists, is proof enough that evolution is a religion.

Christians should therefore find it untenable to believe in evolution— they should only believe in creation. Christians who reject that God is the Creator are denying one of the fundamental truths of Christianity. By doing so, they are actually denying the authority of Scripture. Christians who are confronted with the question 'Evolution or creation?' need to think very carefully about how to answer. If they answer 'Evolution', they need to be aware of exactly what they are denying and where they are putting their trust and faith. It is significant to note, for example, that in an interview, Sir Julian Huxley declared that he was an atheist and that Darwin's real achievement was to remove the whole idea of God as the Creator of organisms from the sphere of rational discussion.[13]

The sovereignty of God in creation

That God is the Creator of all things is stated clearly in Genesis 1:

- '… God created the heavens and the earth' (v. 1)
- 'Thus God made the firmament, and divided the waters which were under the firmament from the waters which were above the firmament' (v. 7)
- 'Then God made two great lights: the greater light to rule the day, and the lesser light to rule the night' (v. 16)
- 'He [God] made the stars also' (v. 16)
- 'So God created great sea creatures and every living thing that moves, with which the waters abounded, according to their kind, and every winged bird according to its kind' (v. 21)
- 'And God made the beast of the earth according to its kind, cattle according to its kind, and everything that creeps on the earth according to its kind' (v. 25)
- 'So God created man in His own image; in the image of God He created him; male and female He created them' (v. 27).

It is usually at this point that some will argue that there is a difference between the verbs 'create' and 'make' (the Hebrew words are *barah* and *asah*, respectively), and that it is incorrect to say that God *created* all things because there are some things which God 'made'. That these two words are synonymous in Genesis 1, however, is seen clearly from verses 26 and 27; the word *asah* (to make) is used in verse 26 and *barah* (to create) is used in verse 27 to describe the same act. Let nothing therefore rob our perception of the full extent and supernatural nature of the work done by God's initial creative acts.

Additional teaching about creation is found in the New Testament. We are told by the writer of the book of Hebrews that the Father who planned creation accomplished this through his Son: 'God, who at various times and in various ways spoke in time past to the fathers by the prophets, has in these last days spoken to us by His Son, whom He has appointed heir of all things, through whom also he made the worlds' (Heb. 1:1–2). And this is confirmed by the apostle John in his Gospel:

In the beginning was the Word, and the Word was with God, and the Word was God. He was in the beginning with God. All things were made through Him, and without Him nothing was made that was made ... He was in the world, and the world was made through Him, and the world did not know Him ... And the Word became flesh and dwelt among us, and we beheld His glory, the glory as of the only begotten of the Father, full of grace and truth. (John 1:1–3, 10, 14)

Here we read about the Word—the *logos*—the Son of God who was not only 'with God' but also 'was God'. This Word 'became flesh'—that is, became a man in the form of the Lord Jesus Christ. This same Word created 'all things'—that is, everything in the space–time continuum.

That it was Jesus Christ, the Son of God, who created all things is further confirmed by what the apostle Paul wrote to the believers in Colosse: 'For by Him [God's Son] all things were created that are in heaven and that are on earth, visible and invisible, whether thrones or dominions or principalities or powers. All things were created through Him and for Him. And He is before all things and in Him all things consist' (Col. 1:16–17). Furthermore, Scripture also teaches us that creation was accomplished by the power of the Holy Spirit: 'And the Spirit of God was hovering over the face of the waters' (Gen. 1:2); 'By His Spirit He adorned the heavens' (Job 26:13).

From these Scriptures and others (see, for example, Job 38:4–41 and Isaiah 40:12–31) we see that the creation was wholly of God. He needed neither human agency nor counsellor—and he certainly did not need a committee to advise him! Looking carefully at the Scriptures, we see that there is no scope for such theories as theistic evolution to water down God's full and total involvement in the whole of creation, as though he were not able to undertake and finish the task of creating everything unaided.

Not only is the creation *of* God, but the Bible teaches that it is also *for* him. He alone is responsible to no one. Of his own will he created, because he wanted to do so: 'The LORD has made all for Himself' (Prov. 16:4); 'For by Him [God's Son] all things were created that are in heaven and that are on earth, visible and invisible, whether thrones or dominions or principalities or powers. All things were created through Him and for Him' (Col. 1:16); 'You are worthy, O Lord, to receive glory and honor and power; for You created all things, and by Your will they exist and were created' (Rev. 4:11).

When considering the doctrine of creation, then, there is no room for human self-assurance or self-centredness. As William Kethe, the hymnist, penned,

The Lord, ye know, is God indeed;
Without our aid He did us make.[14]

A similar pattern is found when we consider salvation, for this, too, owes nothing to human initiative: 'But as many as received Him, to them He gave the right to become children of God, to those who believe in His name: who were born, not of blood, nor of the will of the flesh, nor of the will of man, but of God' (John 1:12–13); 'Of His own will He brought us forth by the word of truth, that we might be a kind of firstfruits of His creatures' (James 1:18).

Just as the physical creation was planned and accomplished without human aid, so it was with salvation—this, too, was planned and has been accomplished by God alone, as clearly taught in the Scriptures: 'Jesus answered, "Most assuredly, I say to you, unless one is born of water and the Spirit, he cannot enter the kingdom of God"' (John 3:5).

But when the kindness and the love of God our Savior toward man appeared, not by works of righteousness which we have done, but according to His mercy He saved us, through the washing of regeneration and renewing of the Holy Spirit, whom He poured out on us abundantly through Jesus Christ our Savior, that having been justified by His grace we should become heirs according to the hope of eternal life.

(Titus 3:4–7)

It may be seen plainly, then, that just as the original work of creation was wholly divine, being both *of* God and *for* him, so it was with the work of salvation. How all-embracing are the words of the apostle Paul in his letter addressed to the saints in Rome: 'For of Him and through Him and to Him are all things, to whom be glory forever. Amen' (Rom. 11:36). No wonder the atheist is antagonistic towards the doctrine of special creation! This explains why atheists get so enraged when they are confronted with this doctrine. Their hatred is aroused by having to acknowledge their total inability to exist apart from God, in whom they don't believe! How precious to atheists is the theory of evolution with which they endeavour to banish God, and any accountability to him, from their minds!

The fall and restoration of the creation

In Genesis 1:31 we read, 'Then God saw everything that He had made, and indeed it was very good.' This, however, is in stark contrast to what the apostle Paul wrote in his epistle to the Romans: 'For we know that the whole creation groans and labors with birth pangs together until now' (Rom. 8:22). What happened to bring about such a change—from such a perfect and good creation that even the angels shouted for joy when it was created (Job 38:7), to one that is likened to a woman who is groaning and travailing (as the King James Version puts it) in the pains of childbirth? The answer to this question is found in Genesis 2–3.

In Genesis 2 we read the account of the creation of Adam and Eve. This is not a *different* account of the creation of humans from that in Genesis 1—it is simply a fuller account. In Genesis 2:16–17, we read, 'And the LORD God commanded the man, saying, "Of every tree of the garden you may freely eat; but of the tree of the knowledge of good and evil you shall not eat, for in the day that you eat of it you shall surely die [or: 'dying you shall die']."'

In the next chapter, however, we read of Adam's eating the forbidden fruit of this tree in complete disobedience to the word of God. Why did he do this? The Bible records that Satan, in the form of a serpent, deceived Eve by introducing an element of doubt into her mind, causing her to question

God's word by asking her, 'Has God indeed said … ?' (3:1). He also lied to her, telling her that she would not die if she ate the forbidden fruit. Today, Satan is using the same tactics that he used in the Garden of Eden. He is still causing people to question and doubt what God has said in his Word. He still attempts to make people reject what is recorded in the Bible— especially in the early chapters of Genesis. No wonder these chapters come under such attack, for it is in them that we see not only the greatness of God, but also the subtlety of Satan.

Eve ate the forbidden fruit and gave it to her husband, and he also ate it. Adam's sin—eating the fruit of the tree of the knowledge of good and evil (note that the Bible does not say it was an apple[15])—is referred to as 'the Fall'. This resulted in many changes to God's creation: Adam and Eve knew immediately that they were naked and they tried to hide themselves from God; women's conception was increased; women would experience pain when they gave birth to their children; the ground was cursed; thorns and thistles started to grow; and, most significantly, death was introduced.

One of the most frequently asked questions is: Why is there death and suffering in the world? The answer is: Because of Adam's sin. Ultimately, Adam is responsible. When God confronted Adam about his sin, Adam first blamed Eve and then tried to blame God, because it was God who had given Eve to him (Gen. 3:12). Nothing is new. People today try to blame God for all the sin, disease, suffering and death that is in the world, instead of blaming Adam and the fact that we all continue to follow Adam's pattern by sinning.

The point about the introduction of death into the world as a result of Adam's sin is very interesting and has a number of consequences. The Bible teaches very clearly that death is the result of sin—Romans 6:23 states that death is the 'wages' of sin. Adam and Eve began to die physically from the moment that they ate the forbidden fruit—not because the fruit was intrinsically harmful, but because they had sinned against God by not obeying his command not to eat it. Eventually they died— according to Genesis 5:5, it took Adam 930 years to die. God is not slack concerning his promises; it may take years for God's Word to come to pass, but come to pass it does!

The introduction of physical death had far wider implications than the death of Adam, for it resulted in the deaths of all who have lived and will live on this planet, as the following two verses show:

- 'For since by man [referring to Adam] came death ...' (1 Cor. 15:21)
- 'Therefore, just as through one man sin entered the world, and death through sin, and thus death spread to all men, because all sinned ...' (Rom. 5:12).

Furthermore, far more is implied by the term 'death' than the mere fact of coming to an end of life instead of living for ever. Death also means the loss of that quality of life that God intended humans to have—a life in complete communion with him. Because of Adam's sin, he (and consequently all his descendants) was cut off spiritually from God and became spiritually dead. The Bible refers to people as being 'dead in trespasses and sins' (Eph. 2:1) when in fact they are very much alive physically. It is only when a person is born again of the Spirit of God (John 3:5) that he or she is made alive spiritually—although in this life there can never be a complete restoration to that complete and perfect spiritual communion with God. This helps throw further light on the effects of the Fall.

We have already seen that physical death is a direct consequence of sin. A very well-known Bible verse sums this up concisely while at the same time hinting at how much more than mere physical decay was implied by death passing on to all people: '... for all have sinned and fall short of the glory of God' (Rom. 3:23).

Humans were originally made in 'the image and glory of God' (1 Cor. 11:7). Through sin, they lost not only that glory but also their relationship with God, so that they naturally became separated from the life of the Creator—this is known as spiritual death. Not only this, but 'the whole creation groans and labors with birth pangs together' (Rom. 8:22), suffering from the effects of the catastrophic loss. The loss to both the human race and to creation will only be restored when the work of God in redemption is complete: 'For the earnest expectation of the creation eagerly waits for the revealing of the sons of God. For the creation was subjected to futility, not willingly, but because of Him who subjected it in hope; because the creation itself also will be delivered from the bondage of corruption into the glorious liberty of the children of God' (Rom. 8:19–21).

The reversal of the effects of the Fall and the restoration of humans to the glory of God is, then, the ultimate objective of our salvation:

- 'For whom He foreknew, He also predestined to be conformed to the image of His Son, that He might be the firstborn among many brethren. Moreover whom He predestined, these He also called; whom He called, these He also justified; and whom He justified, these He also glorified' (Rom. 8:29–30)
- 'But we all, with unveiled face, beholding as in a mirror the glory of the Lord, are being transformed into the same image from glory to glory, just as by the Spirit of the Lord' (2 Cor. 3:18)
- 'Therefore, having been justified by faith, we have peace with God through our Lord Jesus Christ, through whom also we have access by faith into this grace in which we stand, and rejoice in hope of the glory of God' (Rom. 5:1–2).

One of the cardinal factors in the plan of God to restore us was that God himself was to take upon himself the likeness of sinful flesh: 'But when the fullness of the time had come, God sent forth His Son, born of a woman, born under the law, to redeem those who were under the law, that we might receive the adoption as sons' (Gal. 4:4–5). At the right time, the Son of God, the Lord Jesus Christ, became flesh and suffered so that we could be reconciled to our Creator:

- 'For Christ also suffered once for sins, the just for the unjust, that He might bring us to God, being put to death in the flesh but made alive by the Spirit' (1 Peter 3:18)
- 'For it was fitting for Him, for whom are all things and by whom are all things, in bringing many sons to glory, to make the captain of their salvation perfect through sufferings' (Heb. 2:10).

To comprehend this fully, we must appreciate the incarnation and the virgin birth—the fact that God, who is absolutely holy, resided in a body of human flesh. Jesus Christ was God in human flesh—it was not *sinful* flesh but was in the *likeness* of sinful flesh (Rom. 8:3).

The purpose of the incarnation was so that God could be the Saviour as well as Creator. In his humanity, however, God had to be 'holy, harmless, undefiled, separate from sinners' (Heb. 7:26). Had Jesus Christ's body been made by the normal process of reproduction, such a statement could not have applied. The body of Jesus Christ was specially prepared by God, and this is why he had to be born of the virgin Mary: 'Therefore, when He came into the world, He said: "Sacrifice and offering You did not desire, but a body You have prepared for Me"' (Heb. 10:5). The Greek word that is translated 'prepared' in this verse is the verb *katartizo*. What is remarkable is that this same word is translated as 'framed' in Hebrews 11:3: 'By faith we understand that the worlds were framed [*katartizo*] by the word of God, so that the things which are seen were not made of things which are visible.' In other words, the same processes that were employed in the preparation of Jesus Christ's body were used in the 'framing' of the worlds—that is, special creation. In his perfect body, Jesus Christ, the Son of God dwelt among the people of the world. In his body, Jesus Christ:

- 'grew and became strong in spirit, filled with wisdom; and the grace of God was upon Him' (Luke 2:40)
- 'increased in wisdom and stature, and in favor with God and men' (Luke 2:52).

The main purpose of God's intervention into the affairs of man (as many like to put it) was to procure our salvation. To do this, the sinless Son of God not only had to die on the cross of Calvary, but on that same cross he who knew no sin also had to be made sin and bear the punishment for our sin: 'For He [God] made Him who knew no sin [Jesus Christ] to be sin for us, that we might become the righteousness of God in Him' (2 Cor. 5:21).[16] Hence the perfect and sinless Son of God took our sins upon himself and was sacrificed for us—so that our sins could be forgiven. This, then, is the gospel, the Good News: sin which placed a barrier between God and humankind has been dealt with by God; '… the blood of Jesus Christ His Son cleanses us from all sin' (1 John 1:7).

This is the *only way* to God—in and through Jesus Christ, God's only begotten Son. But this is only part of the gospel message. The apostle Paul wrote the following to those in the church at Corinth: 'For I delivered to you first of all that which I also received: that Christ died for our sins according to the Scriptures, and that He was buried, and that He rose again the third day according to the Scriptures' (1 Cor. 15:3–4). Here is good news indeed—Jesus Christ is alive! No wonder those who kept guard over Christ's tomb and the religious leaders of the day could not produce the body of Christ after his death—he had risen from the dead! No wonder the writer to the Hebrews could write, 'Therefore He is also able to save to the uttermost those who come to God through Him, since He always lives to make intercession for them' (Heb. 7:25); and '… how shall we escape if we neglect so great a salvation …?' (Heb. 2:3).

So far, we have considered the perfection of the original creation, the Fall and its consequences for us and the whole physical creation, and God's plan to restore us to our former glory. This plan is referred to in the Scriptures as 'God's new creation'. This new creation began with salvation and will be complete when God makes all things new: 'Now I saw a new heaven and a new earth, for the first heaven and the first earth had passed away' (Rev. 21:1). In 2 Peter 3:9–14 we are warned to be mindful of this—and, indeed, we should be.

Although someone who is redeemed is referred to as God's new creation in 2 Corinthians 5:17, as yet there is not a full restoration to the original creation. We are told in the Scriptures that those who are redeemed possess a 'guarantee' of it (Eph. 1:14) and have 'tasted' of the heavenly gift (Heb. 6:4); its fullness, however, is still to come. Although we rejoice in the hope of the glory of God (Rom. 5:2), and although we can experience a progressive restoration even now towards it (2 Cor. 3:18), the full unveiling of the children of God in the full liberty of the glory of God is yet to come (Rom. 8:18–23). The regeneration of the Holy Spirit (Titus 3:5), which the Christian has already experienced, is a foretaste of the regeneration yet to come (Matt. 19:28). The creation will only be restored to its former glory when God creates a new heaven and a new earth; then will be fulfilled the vision of Isaiah:

The wolf also shall dwell with the lamb,
The leopard shall lie down with the young goat,
The calf and the young lion and the fatling together;
And a little child shall lead them.
The cow and the bear shall graze;
Their young ones shall lie down together;
And the lion shall eat straw like the ox.
The nursing child shall play by the cobra's hole,

And the weaned child shall put his hand in the viper's den.
They shall not hurt nor destroy in all My holy mountain,
For the earth shall be full of the knowledge of the LORD
As the waters cover the sea.   (Isa. 11:6–9)

'The wolf and the lamb shall feed together,
The lion shall eat straw like the ox,
And dust shall be the serpent's food.
They shall not hurt nor destroy in all My holy mountain,'
Says the LORD.   (Isa. 65:25)

At last the glory of the Lord will once again fill the whole earth, as prophesied by the prophet Habakkuk: 'For the earth will be filled with the knowledge of the glory of the LORD, as the waters cover the sea' (Hab. 2:14). Amen!

Conclusion

In this chapter we have seen the scriptural evidence for the fact that God is the Creator of all things. The Christian's acceptance of this doctrine is based on faith—faith in the authority of the Word of the living God who is wholly unaccountable to anyone, and *by* whom, as well as *for* whom, all things were created. No wonder this faith is so contrary to the faith of evolutionists, for whom the doctrine of special creation is so repugnant. Finally, we have considered how the original creation was marred and how the restoration of the whole creation is part and parcel of the message of the gospel. The creation message is, therefore, not a side issue or something we can ignore in order to keep the peace and unity with other believers. Rather, it is foundational to the understanding of our need of salvation.

Notes

1 **Mark Twain,** quoted at: twainquotes.com/Faith.html.
2 **Dr John Whitcomb** in an audio tape message entitled 'The Creator and His Methods' in the series *The Bible and Science* (Send the Light Trust, c.1976).
3 **Mark Twain,** quoted at: twainquotes.com/Mississippi.html.

4 Ibid.

5 Richard Dawkins, quoted in 'Faith v Fact', 7 January 2005 at: guardian.co.uk. Until his retirement in September 2008, Professor Richard Dawkins held the Charles Simonyi Chair for the Public Understanding of Science at the University of Oxford.

6 Edwin G. Conklin, *Man Real and Ideal*, quoted in Norman Macbeth, *Darwin Retried* (New York: Dell, 1971), p. 127.

7 Charles Darwin, *On the Origin of Species* (London: Penguin, 1968), p. 293.

8 Whitcomb, 'The Creator and His Methods'.

9 Exact reference not known.

10 L. T. More, *The Dogma of Evolution* (Princeton: Princeton University Press, 1925), p. 304.

11 See section entitled 'Atheism and Evolution' in Chapter 9 and also **Dr Tommy Mitchell** and **Dr A. J. Monty White,** 'Is Evolution a Religion?' in **Ken Ham,** (ed.), *The New Answers Book 2* (Green Forest, AR: Master Books, 2008), pp. 207–217.

12 Laura Sheahen and **Dr Richard Dawkins,** 'The Problem with God: Interview with Richard Dawkins', 11 November 2005, at: www.beliefnet.com/News/Science-Religion/2005/11/The-Problem-With-God-Interview-With-Richard-Dawkins.aspx.

13 Sir Julian Huxley, '*At Random*: A Television Preview', interview for CBS, 21 November 1959; transcript published in *Tax*, vol. 3, pp. 41–65 (1960).

14 William Kethe, 'All People that on Earth Do Dwell', 1561.

15 The reason why the forbidden fruit is thought of as being an apple is because in the Latin Vulgate version of the Bible, the word 'evil' is quite correctly translated by the Latin word *malus*. The Latin word for apple is also *malus*, so people began to think of an apple when they read the Latin translation of 'the fruit of the tree of the knowledge of good and evil'.

16 This doctrine of penal substitution has been rejected by many so-called Christians since the publication of **Steve Chalke** and **Alan Mann's** *The Lost Message of Jesus* (Grand Rapids, MI: Zondervan, 2003). Steve Chalke and his co-author reject the idea of God's having punished Christ in our stead, calling it 'cosmic child abuse'.

Theistic evolution?

Many Christians believe that scientists have proven that evolution has occurred and that it is fact. There are three main reasons for this. The *first* reason is that the education systems in the West indoctrinate children into believing that evolution is a fact.[1] This is further strengthened by the implication that only those who are uneducated reject evolution. The *second* reason is that the media propagates evolution as the *only* explanation for the origin and development of life on earth. This is further strengthened by the fact that, when those holding creationist views are interviewed on the radio or television, they and their views are usually ridiculed. The *third* reason is that many influential church leaders believe in evolution and they are vocal in their opposition to a creationist interpretation of the origin and development of life on earth.

Such Christians want to believe that God is the Creator of all things. What they therefore do is come to the conclusion that God used evolution to bring about his creation. In other words, they believe in 'theistic evolution'—that is, that evolution has occurred but that somehow God controlled the processes. They believe this without really thinking about the implications of a compromise position, for a compromise position it is—as we shall see.

I am sure that many who read this book will be surprised to realize that many pastors, elders and deacons are totally opposed to the teaching of creation in their churches. When I was Chief Executive of Answers in Genesis, I encountered churches that refused to have a speaker from Answers in Genesis because the pastor or one or more of the leadership team did not want the creationist view to be presented in the church—even though members of the church wanted a speaker to come. Sometimes it was the pastor who wanted to hold such a meeting and one or more of the elders or deacons did not want to have it. On more than one occasion I also experienced situations when a youth leader arranged to take the church's youth away for the duration of the meeting(s) in order to prevent their hearing what the Bible taught concerning creation.

In the UK and USA, most Bible colleges do not teach creation but theistic evolution as the way of explaining how things came into existence. It is easy to determine why this has happened in the UK. In order to get their qualifications recognized by the state and by universities, Bible colleges have had their courses and qualifications accredited by a university (usually, but not always, the local one). This has enabled their students to get help towards their tuition fees and what amounts to interest-free loans from the state for their living expenses while they study. However, in order to get their courses accredited in this way, the Bible colleges have had to compromise their teachings, especially about the early chapters of Genesis; they have to teach that these chapters cannot be interpreted as being historically accurate.

There are a number of prominent and influential church leaders on both sides of the Atlantic who oppose creation in favour of evolution. One such man, who has had influence in the Anglican community, is Richard Harries, now Lord Harries of Pentregarth, the former Bishop of Oxford. In an article published in the *Observer* on 16 April 2006, Richard Harries made reference to his opposition to the creationist position and stated that creationism 'should not be taught in schools'.[2] Steve Chalke is a prominent Baptist leader who also opposes the teaching of creation in schools. In the UK, Steve Chalke is a well-known evangelical, TV personality and adviser to the UK government on religious matters. He is the founder of Oasis Trust, an organization which undertakes mission, healthcare, education and housing initiatives not only in the UK, but across the globe. When the Oasis Trust announced in 2004 that it was planning to open a new faith-based Academy School in Enfield in North London, Steve Chalke said that the creationist view of origins would not be taught there. He was quoted as saying, 'My personal belief is that ... those who wish to read into Genesis chapter one that God made the world in six days ... are not being honest and scholarly. It won't be taught in the school because I *think it's rubbish*. It's a bizarre thing to claim the Bible suggests that' (emphasis added).[3]

In the USA, Hugh Ross and his very popular Reasons to Believe website (www.reasons.org) has had a profound influence on Christian thinking in the area of origins and has caused many to believe in theistic evolution. Hugh Ross's problem is that he recognizes not one, but two revelations from God—God's Word (Scripture) and God's world (nature), as stated clearly in the statement of belief found on his website.4 Although he maintains that these two revelations never contradict each other, Hugh Ross nevertheless accepts the evolutionary account of the history of the origin and development of life on earth, rather than the simple account that we read in the early chapters of Genesis. Herein lies the danger, as is pointed out by John MacArthur in his excellent book entitled *The Battle for the Beginning*: 'Scripture, not science, is the ultimate test of all truth. And the further evangelicalism gets from that conviction, the less evangelical and more humanistic it becomes.'5

In general, there are two different interpretations of the early chapters of Genesis that are held by those who believe in theistic evolution. One proposes that these early chapters are poetic and/or mythical—the result of oral traditions handed down by the patriarchs in poetic or story form in order to explain problems such as sin, suffering, death, language differences and so on. This interpretation maintains that the early chapters of Genesis are not historical but contain an element of truth in them. The other interpretation teaches that the early chapters of Genesis contain a simplified historical account of the creation and early history of the earth which in no way conflicts with the evolutionary account. It is usually—but not always—the case that more liberal-minded Christians follow the first approach, whereas those who wish to try to maintain their fundamentalist views tend to follow the second. In the next couple of sections of this chapter, we will examine these two approaches.

Is Genesis mythical or symbolic?

Does the Bible teach that Genesis 1–11 is poetic or mythical? This is a question that must be answered. The Bible teaches that 'All Scripture is given by inspiration of God' (2 Tim. 3:16), and it can be seen from 1 Timothy 5:18 that both Old and New Testaments are included in the phrase 'all Scripture'. This means that Genesis 1–11 was written under the inspiration of the Holy Spirit. With this in mind, we have to ask: Are the early chapters of Genesis straightforward history, or is God trying to teach us lessons in these chapters by telling us stories that did not happen—that is, by using parables or poetry?

This question has been adequately answered by Dr James Barr, who, it should be pointed out, did not actually believe that Genesis was true history. However, in a personal communication to the late David C. C. Watson on 23 April 1984, Professor Barr, who at the time was Regius Professor of Hebrew at the University of Oxford, wrote,

Probably, so far as I know, there is no Professor of Hebrew or Old Testament at any world-class university who does not believe that the writer(s) of Genesis 1–11 intended to convey to their readers the idea that:

(a) creation took place in a series of six days which were the same as the days of 24 hours we now experience;

(b) the figures contained in the genealogies provided by simple addition a chronology from the beginning of the world up to the later stages in the biblical story;

(c) Noah's flood was understood to be world-wide and extinguish all human and animal life except for those in the ark.[6]

If this is the case, why do the majority of Hebrew scholars insist that the early chapters of Genesis need to be reinterpreted as mythical, allegorical or legendary? The simple answer is 'evolution'. These scholars assume that evolution has occurred, so they reinterpret the early chapters of Genesis to fit the story of evolution.

However, the conclusion that the early chapters of Genesis are straightforward history was reinforced by Dr J. W. Milner in a lecture entitled 'Creation in Six Days' given to the Trinitarian Bible Society in Leicester in 1969. He pointed out that the language used in Genesis 1–3 is that of narrative, and that what we read is sober history. Dr Milner reminded his audience that when we read these chapters, we are not reading Hebrew poetry nor the vision of a prophet. He continued,

If we were to read these chapters without bringing to them any preconceived notions of our own and without thinking 'Well, I believe this and therefore I must turn the Scriptures to fit in with what I believe'—if we set that on one side and come to the Scriptures with an open mind, then we could only come to one conclusion. If we were honest, we would have to admit that the writer, Moses, is describing just what happened … proof, then, that the first chapters of Genesis are to be taken literally, is from the language of the passages. It is the same language which is used when we read about Abraham, when we read about Isaac and Jacob. We are reading about things that actually happened.7

Professor Edward J. Young, who was Professor of Old Testament at Westminster Theological Seminary from 1936 until his death in 1968, reached the same conclusion in his fine monograph *Studies in Genesis One*, in which he concluded,

Genesis one is not poetry or saga or myth, but straightforward, trustworthy history, and inasmuch as it is a divine revelation, accurately records those matters of which it speaks. That Genesis one is historical may be seen from these considerations:

1) It sustains an intimate relationship with the remainder of the book. The remainder of the book (i.e. The Generations) presupposes the Creation Account, and the Creation Account prepares for what follows. The two portions of Genesis are integral parts of the book and complement one another.

2) The characteristics of Hebrew poetry are lacking. There are poetic accounts of the creation and these form a striking contrast to Genesis one.

3) The New Testament regards certain events mentioned in Genesis one as actually having taken place. We may safely allow the New Testament to be our interpreter of this mighty first chapter of the Bible.8

This last point is crucial. Let us examine the attitude of Jesus Christ and the New Testament writers, not only to Genesis 1, but also to the other early chapters of Genesis. Did they take the early chapters of Genesis literally, or did they treat them as poetic or mythical? By examining their attitudes towards this part of the Bible, we will see what our attitude should be.

In Mark 10:2–9 we read the account of how some Pharisees came to Jesus Christ and asked him the question, 'Is it lawful for a man to divorce his wife?' Jesus answered their question by referring them back to the

Genesis account of the creation and quoting Genesis 1:27 and 2:24 in his answer recorded for us in Mark 10:6–8: 'But from the beginning of the creation, God "made them male and female". "For this reason a man shall leave his father and mother and be joined to his wife, and the two shall become one flesh"; so then they are no longer two, but one flesh.' (The parallel account of this incident is found in Matt. 19:3–9.) Reading this account, it is obvious that the Lord Jesus Christ accepted the Genesis account of the creation of man and woman as being historical rather than figurative. By quoting from Genesis chapters 1 and 2 regarding the creation of Adam and Eve, Jesus showed irrefutably that he accepted these parts of Genesis as being literal. He did not believe them to be symbolic, mythical or allegorical. If this is how the Lord Jesus Christ interpreted the story of the creation of humankind, why should we reject such an interpretation and choose to believe something different?

The fact that the Lord Jesus Christ believed Noah to have been a historical person and the universal Flood described in Genesis to have been a real historical event is established in Matthew's Gospel. In Matthew 24:37–39, Jesus Christ is recorded as saying,

But as the days of Noah were, so also will the coming of the Son of Man be. For as in the days before the flood, they were eating and drinking, marrying and giving in marriage, until the day that Noah entered the ark, and did not know until the flood came and took them all away, so also will the coming of the Son of Man be.

In the parallel account given in Luke 17:26–27, the last part of Jesus Christ's warning is worded '… until the day that Noah entered the ark, and the flood came and destroyed them all'.

These verses, taken in their contexts, show that Jesus Christ took the account of the Flood recorded in Genesis 6–9 as being historical. He took these chapters literally. He accepted this part of Genesis as fact, not fiction. He did not consider Noah to be a mythical character, nor did he believe that the Flood was a legend. Again, we must ask ourselves: If this is how the Lord Jesus Christ interpreted the story of the Flood, why should we reject such an interpretation and choose to believe something different?

If we turn to the apostle Paul, we see that he, too, accepted the early chapters of Genesis as being literally and historically true. We can see this when he spoke to the Athenians on the Areopagus (Mars Hill)—the account of this is found in Acts 17:16–34. In his sermon, he declared God to be the Creator of 'the world and everything in it' (v. 24). Paul also believed in a literal Adam and referred to him on a number of occasions as he hammered out his teachings. For example, in his letter to the Romans he wrote,

Nevertheless death reigned from Adam to Moses, even over those who had not sinned according to the likeness of the transgression of Adam, who is a type of Him who was to come. But the free gift is not like the offense. For if by the one man's offense many died, much more the grace of God and the gift by the grace of the one Man, Jesus Christ, abounded to many.   (Rom. 5:14–15)

Similarly, in his first letter to the Corinthians he wrote, 'For as in Adam all die, even so in Christ all shall be made alive' (1 Cor. 15:22); 'And so it is written, "The first man Adam became a living being." The last Adam became a life-giving spirit' (1 Cor. 15:45). And in his first letter to Timothy we read, 'For Adam was formed first, then Eve. And Adam was not deceived, but the woman being deceived, fell into transgression' (1 Tim. 2:13–14).

We can see that in his arguments, the apostle Paul accepted not only the fact that Adam was a real historical person, but that all the events surrounding him—Eve, sin, death and so on—were also real. He did not see them as being in any way symbolic, mythical or poetic. For example, Paul did not write, 'For as in a symbol, myth or allegory all die', but he wrote, 'as in *Adam*', showing that he believed in a literal, historical Adam—the first human being, the one from whom we are all descended.

Turning to the Gospel of Luke, we find a similar testimony to the literal truth of Genesis. In Luke 3:23–38 the genealogy of Jesus Christ through Mary, his mother, is meticulously recorded. From the end of verse 34 to verse 38, Luke gives the genealogy from Abraham back to Adam, following the genealogies given in Genesis 11 (for the genealogy of Abraham back to Noah) and Genesis 5 (for the genealogy of Noah back to Adam). In other words, Luke accepted that the people recorded in those chapters were real people who lived real lives and had real families. These people lived in history—they were not mythical or legendary. When Luke had traced Jesus's genealogy to Adam, the first man, he was moved by the Holy Spirit to write that Adam was 'the son of God' (Luke 2:38), for God had indeed given birth to him when he fashioned and formed him from the dust of the ground and breathed into him 'the breath of life' (Gen. 2:7).

Finally, the apostle Peter revealed his belief in a literal universal Flood when he wrote in his second epistle that 'the world that then existed perished, being flooded with water' (2 Peter 3:6).

All the verses cited above demonstrate the attitude of the Lord Jesus Christ, Paul, Luke and Peter to the early chapters of Genesis. They show that they interpreted them literally and historically—there is not even a hint that any one of them considered the Genesis account of the creation and early history of the earth to be in any way poetic, mythical or allegorical. This, then, must be our attitude to these chapters—we too are to regard Genesis 1–11 as a true historical record of what actually happened, written under the inspiration of Almighty God. The account was written as history, for it is history.

Is Genesis evolutionary?

Can the early chapters of Genesis be interpreted as a record of the alleged evolutionary history of the cosmos and of the development of life on earth? There are two main reasons why people believe that the early chapters of Genesis can be interpreted in terms of evolution. The first reason is that many have been brainwashed into believing that evolution is a fact, and they do not wish to appear to be foolish or ignorant by rejecting the 'fact' of evolution. We will address the scientific arguments about evolution in later chapters; readers will then be able to see whether they are indeed foolish or ignorant to reject evolution.

The second major reason why people believe that the early chapters of Genesis can be interpreted in terms of evolution is because they think that the biblical account of origins occurs in the same order as the order proposed by the evolutionists. They will argue, for example, that both accounts begin with the words 'In the beginning'. They will also argue that each of the days in Genesis 1 are not to be interpreted as literal days, but are in fact long periods of time which correspond to one or more of the Geological Periods.

Although there is much speculation about which Geological Period(s) corresponds to which day, some argue that the first day of Genesis 1 corresponds to the time when the earth was going through the long geological processes that formed it. The events of Day Two are sometimes seen as the events that occurred on the earth during the Cambrian, Ordovician, Silurian and Devonian Periods, and that the abundant plant life described as created on Day Three in Genesis 1 is a description of what is called the Carboniferous Period in Europe (or the Mississippian and Pennsylvanian Periods in the USA), when most coal was deposited. The creation of the heavenly bodies on Day Four is interpreted as being a description of the desert conditions that occurred in the Permo-Triassic Period, while the creation of the birds and fish on Day Five is seen to be a description of their evolution during the Jurassic and Cretaceous times. Day Six of Genesis 1, when the mammals and finally humans were created, is made to correspond to the Tertiary and Quaternary times. And yes, of course, we are now living in Day Seven!

However, on closer inspection, it can be seen that there is no real correlation between the order of events outlined in Genesis 1 and the order proposed by evolutionists. The discrepancies are elucidated very clearly in Table 1, which has been taken from an article entitled 'Evolution vs. Creation: The Order of Events Matters!' by Dr Terry Mortensen.[9] This table shows that there is no harmony between creation and evolution, and that theistic evolution is based on the false premise that the Genesis account of origins occurs in the same order as that proposed by evolutionists.

A careful study of the order of the events in Genesis 1 therefore shows the impossibility of theistic evolution being reconciled with Scripture. Those who believe in theistic evolution should be aware that they do so, not because the Bible teaches it, but because they prefer to accept the teachings of evolutionists rather than the Word of God.

Having established this, let us now look at the meaning of the Hebrew word *yom* (and its plural form *yamim*), which is translated 'day' (and its plural form 'days') in order to show the inaccuracy of theistic

Table 1: Twenty-three differences between the evolutionary account of the history of the earth and the biblical account of creation

	Evolution	Creation
1	Sun before earth	Earth before sun
2	Dry land before sea	Sea before dry land
3	Atmosphere before sea	Sea before atmosphere
4	Sun before light on earth	Light on earth before sun
5	Stars before earth	Earth before stars
6	Earth at same time as planets	Earth before other planets
7	Sea creatures before land plants	Land plants before sea creatures
8	Earthworms before starfish	Starfish before earthworms
9	Land animals before trees	Trees before land animals
10	Death before man	Man before death
11	Thorns and thistles before man	Man before thorns and thistles
12	TB pathogens & cancer before man (dinosaurs had TB and cancer)	Man before TB pathogens and cancer
13	Reptiles before birds	Birds before reptiles
14	Land mammals before whales	Whales before land animals
15	Simple plants before fruit trees	Fruit trees before other plants*
16	Insects before mammals	Mammals (cattle) before 'creeping things'*
17	Land mammals before bats	Bats before land animals
18	Dinosaurs before birds	Birds before dinosaurs
19	Insects before flowering plants	Flowering plants before insects
20	Sun before plants	Plants before sun
21	Dinosaurs before dolphins	Dolphins before dinosaurs
22	Land reptiles before pterosaurs	Pterosaurs before land reptiles
23	Land insects before flying insects	Flying insects before land insects

* The order maintained in Scripture suggests a slight difference in the timing of their appearance—i.e. they were created on the same day, possibly moments or hours apart.

evolutionists' attempts to translate it in such a way as to justify their belief in reconciling the days of Genesis 1 with the Geological Periods and times. At the beginning of Chapter 1, we looked very briefly at the meaning and usage of the Hebrew word *yom* and showed that the days in Genesis 1 can only be literal days. This conclusion was reinforced by the late Dr Henry Morris, who was the founder of the Institute for Creation Research:

There is no doubt that the Hebrew word [*yom*] can be used to express time in a general sense. In fact it is actually translated by 'time' 65 times in the King James translation. On the other hand, it is translated by 'day' almost 1200 times. In addition, in the plural, *yamim*, it is translated by 'days' approximately 700 times. It is obvious therefore that the normal meanings of *yom* and *yamim* are 'day' and 'days', respectively.[10]

In the Genesis account of the creation (that is, Gen. 1:1–2:3), the word 'day' occurs thirteen times (and 'days' once). The word 'day' is always the translation of the Hebrew word *yom*. The question that therefore needs to be asked is this: Does the usual meaning of the word apply here, or are the days long periods of time?

It can be shown that the word *yom* means 'day' from the following considerations of the Hebrew:

- The numerical adjective (first, second, third, etc.) indicates that the writer meant a literal day. Similar wording in Numbers 7 can be used for comparison.
- The Hebrew expression 'evening and morning' actually defines what *yom* means—an ordinary day. This same phrase is used in Daniel 8:26, where it clearly means an ordinary day.
- The creation week is used as the basis of the six-days'-work-and-one-day-rest week in the fourth commandment. The words used throughout the text for 'day' and 'days' in the commandment are *yom* and its plural *yamim*:

Remember the Sabbath day [*yom*], to keep it holy. Six days [*yamim*] you shall labor and do all your work, but the seventh day [*yom*] is the Sabbath of the LORD your God … For in six days [*yamim*] the LORD made the heavens and the earth, the sea, and all that is in them, and rested the seventh day [*yamim*]. Therefore the LORD blessed the Sabbath day [*yom*] and hallowed it. (Exod. 20:8–11)

Hence a six-day creation is taught not only in Genesis 1, but also in Exodus—in the middle of the fourth commandment, words of Scripture that were written with the finger of God (Exod. 31:18). In the fourth commandment, nothing could be clearer than that the six creation days and the one rest day of the Lord God are identical in duration with the six work days and one rest day of our seven-day week that he commands us to have. Dr Henry Morris has aptly pointed out that 'the basis for this very precise commandment is trivial and vacuous otherwise'.[11]

Yet, in spite of all this textual evidence, some will still argue by pointing to Genesis 2:4, where the Hebrew word *yom* is translated by the word 'day' but here means a longer period of time than a day—in this case, the whole creation week. They then argue that, because it means a long period of time here, it must also mean a long period of time each time it occurs in Genesis 1. However, in Genesis 2:4 it is obvious from the context that the writer is referring to the creation week: 'This is the history of the heavens and the earth when they were created, in the day that the LORD God made the earth and the heavens, before any plant of the field was in the earth and before any herb of the field had grown' (Gen. 2:4–5a).

A parallel construction is found in Numbers 7:84 in the King James Version, when 'day' refers to the twelve previous days referred to in the earlier verses of the chapter: 'This was the dedication of the altar, in the day when it was anointed, by the princes of Israel …' No one insists on understanding the first 'day', second 'day', and so on and all the way up to the twelfth 'day' in Numbers 7, as long periods of time just because of the use of the word 'day' in Numbers 7:84. So why do so in Genesis 1 because of Genesis 2:4? When 'day' means a long period of time in the Bible, it is obvious from the context; otherwise it means a literal day. The days in Genesis 1 are *not* periods of time—they are literal days.

Yet, in spite of all the linguistic and contextual arguments, some insist that the days in Genesis 1 are not literal days but are periods of a thousand years because of 2 Peter 3:8: 'But, beloved, do not forget this one thing, that with the Lord one day is as a thousand years, and a thousand years as one day.' But arguing that each day in Genesis 1 is a thousand years is not of any use to those wishing to reconcile the Genesis account of creation with evolution, for evolutionists insist that they need *thousands of millions* of years—4,600 million years, to be precise—for the earth to have formed and life on earth to have developed. The 'each day is a thousand years' argument will only give a mere 7,000 years—that is, 4,599,993,000 years fewer than the evolutionists want! The 'each day is a thousand years' argument also falls flat because the last part of the verse reverses the argument; it says that, with the Lord, a thousand years is as a day! So really we are back where we started.

Like every other verse in the Bible, the verse in 2 Peter must not be taken out of its context. In chapter 3 of that epistle, the apostle Peter is addressing those who will come in the last days and will scoff at the promise of the Second Coming of the Lord Jesus Christ. We are told in 2 Peter 3:4 that these scoffers believe that 'all things continue as they were from the beginning of creation'—this is uniformitarianism, the philosophy of evolutionists. The apostle Peter teaches, however, that such people are ignorant; God did not use uniformitarian processes to bring about the universal cataclysmic Flood that caused the world that then existed to perish, and neither will he use those processes to bring about his Second Coming. What is taught in 2 Peter 3:8 is, therefore, the fact that God can accomplish in one day what it appears would need a thousand years to accomplish with uniformitarian processes.

Having seen that the days in Genesis 1 are ordinary days, some ask: How is it possible to have twenty-four-hour periods on the first three creation days in view of the fact that the sun, moon and stars were not created until the fourth day? This is a legitimate question to ask, and it has been adequately answered by Dr John Whitcomb:

The fact that the sun was not created until the fourth day does not make the first three days indefinite periods of time, for on the first day God created a fixed and localized light source in the heaven in reference to which the rotating earth passed through the same kind of day/night cycles as it has since the creation of the sun.[12]

It also needs to be stressed that time is not dependant on the sun, moon and stars for its existence, even though these astronomical bodies were created 'for ... seasons, and for days and years' (Gen. 1:14) and we use them to measure the passing of time. As soon as God created matter, time existed, for many of the properties of matter can only be explained in terms of time. For example, it takes a certain amount of time for an electron to move in its orbit around the nucleus of its atom, and it takes time for atoms and molecules to vibrate and move. A second is now defined using an atomic clock, so the measure of time is *independent* of the sun, moon and stars.

There is one other theological objection to theistic evolution. Most theistic evolutionists tend to argue that the whole of the history of humankind, including the present, belongs to Day Seven. This does not accord with the teachings of Scripture, for in Genesis 2:1–2 we read, 'Thus the heavens and the earth, and all the host of them, were finished. And on the seventh day God ended His work which He had done, and He rested on the seventh day from all His work which He had done.' These verses are written as though the seventh day is in the past—which indeed it is. The theistic evolutionist, however, has to have it in the present. If the theistic evolutionist is correct, it would mean that God is resting and not working at present—something that is denied in the Scriptures:

My help comes from the LORD,
Who made heaven and earth.
He will not allow your foot to be moved;
He who keeps you will not slumber.
Behold, He who keeps Israel
Shall neither slumber nor sleep.   (Ps. 121:2–4)

These verses alone show that God is not resting—he neither slumbers nor sleeps, contrary to the implications of theistic evolution. Furthermore, during his earthly ministry, the Lord Jesus Christ explained that, not only was he working, but so too was God the Father, and that God had been at work until Jesus's time—that is, since his day of rest at the end of his six-day creation: 'But Jesus answered them, "My Father has been working until now, and I have been working"' (John 5:17).

By looking at what theistic evolutionists believe about origins, we have seen that their thinking is muddled, for they accept neither what the Bible teaches nor what the evolutionists teach. Their hybrid ideas do not make sense and, no matter how hard they try, they cannot come up with an account of origins that unites these two irreconcilable explanations. It is ironic that the same Christians who reject a literal view of the early chapters of Genesis, and refer to such a view as being rubbish or illogical, actually accept a view which is so confused and muddled that it makes no sense whatsoever.

Who was Adam?

Every Christian must be able to give a reasoned answer to the question, 'Who was Adam?' Theistic evolutionists do not believe in a literal Adam; they believe that Adam was a composite man. They believe that evolutionary processes eventually produced an animal species that was, to all intents and purposes, human. They think that, at this point, God came to a pair of these 'people' and breathed his spirit into them, thus making them religious animals with spirituality and a moral law. They teach that God remained close to this pair (that is, the Adam and Eve of the Bible) for a while, but that, as they failed to keep his commands, God withdrew his presence from them, sentencing them and the whole of humankind to spiritual death. Because of this, the atoning sacrifice of the Lord Jesus Christ was necessary in order to redeem men and women from this spiritual death imposed upon them. Christ's death has no effect on our physical death, because physical death is the driving force of evolution.

This type of reasoning has been made by the anthropologist E. K. Victor Pearce. He believes that Old Stone Age people were pre-Adamic, and that they were the people that God created in Genesis 1:27. He then argues that he 'finds in the early chapters of Genesis a "cultural zone fossil" which exactly reflects what has long intrigued anthropologists—the "New Stone Age Revolution" in farming and horticulture. The sudden appearance of this new mode of life in the New Stone Age exactly fits the appearance of Adam with his divinely-imparted knowledge "to till the ground and keep it."' In other words, Dr Victor Pearce views Adam as a group of people— the New Stone Age people—rather than as a literal person.[13]

There are, however, five major theological problems with accepting such a view of Adam and his wife Eve:

- If Adam and Eve were religious animals because God had breathed his spirit into them, when did their contemporaries become religious, having an awareness of God?

- The Bible emphatically teaches that Adam was the first human to exist. What, therefore, was the nature of the people (that is, the *Homo sapiens*) who existed before Adam or who were his contemporaries? Were these people soulless and so unable to be saved?
- The Bible teaches quite clearly that Adam was the first person to sin and that, as a result, we all inherit sin because we are all descended from him. What about Adam's human ancestors and his contemporaries—how could they inherit sin, given that they were not descended from him and are in no way able to be described as 'in Adam' (1 Cor. 15:22)?
- The Bible teaches quite clearly that, because of Adam's sin, we all die. We die because we are all descended from him—'For as in Adam all die ...' (1 Cor. 15:22). What about Adam's human ancestors and his contemporaries—were they immortal? Did Adam's contemporaries only start dying when Adam sinned? Even so, this raises the problem that they were not descended from him and could therefore in no way be described as being 'in Adam'.
- The final problem concerns the clear teaching that the Bible makes in Genesis 3:20 that all humans are descended from Eve. How does this affect those people who were descended from Eve's contemporaries? Would this make them 'not human'?

The answers given by theistic evolutionists to these questions may be gleaned by considering the views of the evangelical Christian Professor R. J. Berry, a retired Professor of Genetics from University College, London. He accepts that the New Testament regards Adam as the first parent of the whole human race, but argues that 'it would be incompetent exegesis to regard the Bible's use of "whole human race" as necessarily synonymous with the biological species *Homo sapiens*'.[14] He believes that 'We are human because we have been created in God's image, not because of our membership of a species defined on morphological grounds as *Homo sapiens*; we are qualitatively separable from other hominids not because of any genetical event but because of God's in-breathing.'[15] He then goes on to argue, 'Humanness does not spread from generation to generation in the same way as physically inherited traits; every individual is uniquely endowed with spiritual life by God.

Consequently it is quite possible that, at some time after God had created Adam, he then conferred his image on all members of the same biological species at the time.'[16]

We can see that the main thrust of the theistic evolutionist arguments is that there is a distinction between a member of the species *Homo sapiens* and a human being. The difference is that being human is the result of the act of God's in-breathing as recorded in Genesis 2:7.

But what does the Bible teach regarding Adam? This will clarify our views and will also show the errors of theistic evolutionist views about who Adam was. Genesis 1:26–27 records the creation of people on the sixth creation day. In Genesis 2 a more detailed account of the creation of the first man, Adam, is found: 'And the LORD God formed man of the dust of the ground, and breathed into his nostrils the breath of life; and man became a living being' (Gen. 2:7). There is also an account of the creation of his wife, Eve: 'And the LORD God caused a deep sleep to fall on Adam, and he slept; and He took one of his ribs, and closed up the flesh in its place. Then the rib which the LORD God had taken from man He made [lit. built] into a woman, and He brought her to the man' (Gen. 2:21–22).

The two pertinent questions we need to ask are the following: Is the biblical account of the creation of Adam and his wife, Eve, evolutionary in its teaching? Does the Bible teach that Adam and Eve were products of evolutionary processes operating over millions of years? Although the answer to both these questions is a resounding 'No!', theistic evolutionists still try to read evolution into the Scriptures, arguing that the 'dust of the ground' mentioned in Genesis 2:7 is the Bible's way of referring to the evolutionary descent (or should it be ascent?) of humans via the various life forms (uni-cellular organisms ➜ multi-cellular organisms ➜ invertebrates ➜ fish ➜ amphibians ➜ reptiles ➜ mammals) from the first self-replicating molecule which, they maintain, first appeared on the shores of the earth's primeval ocean. This argument, however, is made nonsensical by what God said to Adam in Genesis 3:19:

In the sweat of your face you shall eat bread
Till you return to the ground,
For out if it you were taken;

For dust you are,
And to dust you shall return.

The dust that is referred to here is literal dust and is the same dust mentioned in Genesis 2:7, otherwise the argument used by God would not make sense. It is totally illogical to give 'dust of the ground' one meaning in Genesis 2:7 and a different one in Genesis 3:19, just to fit theistic evolutionist ideas. Adam was the first man—created by God in his image and likeness literally out of the dust of the ground and not as the result of evolutionary processes. Adam was not an advanced hominid,[17] nor was he New Stone Age Man. Such evolutionary views are not supported by the Scriptures.

As we have already seen, the writers of the New Testament believed that Adam was the first man and that he was supernaturally created by God. The truth of his disobedience and fall into sin is vital to the New Testament doctrine of salvation. The apostle Paul argues in Romans 5:12 that not only did sin enter the world because of Adam's sin, but that all men and women have sinned because of Adam's sin. This thought is also expressed by Paul in Romans 3:23, where he states that 'all have sinned and fall short of the glory of God'. Now, sin and death are inextricably joined together—death is the result of sin: '… the wages of sin is death', according to Romans 6:23. However, the second part of that verse is more positive, and also very thrilling: '… but the gift of God is eternal life in Christ Jesus our Lord'. This is the gospel message, and it is a truth that is repeated in 1 Corinthians 15:22, where Paul contrasts the life which we can have in Christ with the death that we all inherit from Adam. Likewise, in Romans 5:19, Paul contrasts the fruit of Adam's disobedience with that of Jesus Christ's obedience.

It is obvious, then, that a literal Adam is absolutely crucial to the plan of salvation, as the following logic shows:

The argument of Paul in Romans 5 depends absolutely for its validity on the fact that, as Jesus was an historical Person, so Adam was an historical person. There cannot be a proper parallel between a mythical Adam and an historical Christ. Adam is as essential to the Christian system of theology as Jesus Christ is. Christ is indeed called 'the second Adam', or 'the last Adam'.[18]

That last point is crucial, for it is nonsense to refer to Christ as 'the last Adam', as the Bible does in 1 Corinthians 15:45, if there was not a 'first Adam'. If the first Adam did not fall from his original perfect state, there is no sin; hence the last Adam died for nothing. It also follows that, if universal death through the first Adam's sin is a myth, so too is the doctrine of the resurrection of the last Adam; our preaching and our faith are then in vain (see 1 Cor. 15:13–22).

We see, therefore, that if the Genesis account is not reliable, the whole basis of the doctrine of the Fall and of salvation collapses. The atheist Dr Richard Dawkins is well aware of this and has actually mocked those Christians who do not believe in the historicity of the Genesis account of the Fall: 'Oh, but of course, the story of Adam and Eve was only ever symbolic, wasn't it? Symbolic? Jesus had himself tortured and executed for a symbolic sin by a non-existent individual. Nobody not brought up in the faith could reach any verdict other than "barking mad!"'[19] This is one of the few times when I can honestly say that I agree wholeheartedly with the sentiments that Richard Dawkins is expressing. If the story of Adam and Eve was symbolic, Jesus Christ's sufferings and sacrifice for our sins are a total nonsense. I often think that atheists' understanding of the theology of original sin is greater than that of the average Christian.

Another militant free-thinking atheist who appreciates the theological importance of the historicity of the early chapters of Genesis is Richard Bozarth. He actually argues for the eradication of the historicity of the Genesis account of Adam and Eve and original sin. Doing this, he suggests, will bring about the end of Christianity: 'Destroy Adam and Eve and the original sin, and in the rubble you will find the sorry remains of the son of god [sic]. Take away the meaning of his death. If Jesus was not the redeemer that died for our sins, and this is what evolution means, then Christianity is nothing.'[20] If you read this quotation carefully, you will see that Richard Bozarth is maintaining that evolution means that Jesus is not the redeemer who died for our sins. This is because, if evolution has occurred, there could have been no Adam, no Eve, no original perfect world, and no Fall; Jesus Christ could not, therefore, be the redeemer, because we would have nothing to be redeemed from. No wonder atheists are evolutionists—it gives them an excuse to ignore their sin and live as they please. No wonder, too, that atheists are not content simply to be atheists but must be 'evangelical' in their opposition to Christianity. Dr Richard Dawkins is a prime example; he is not content merely to disbelieve in God, but must, at every opportunity, attack God (in whom he does not believe) and God's Word (which he does not accept as being God's Word). This would be ludicrous if God did not exist, but it is quite understandable in view of what is written in Psalm 2. There we read that God laughs at those who oppose and plot against him, and that he holds them in derision when he listens to their arguments about getting rid of him.

We see, then, that the Bible teaches unambiguously that Adam was the first man created by Almighty God and that Eve was made by God from a piece of Adam's side. They were made perfect.

The evolutionary view of the history of the human species not only dominates non-Christian philosophy, it also affects Christian thinking to a certain extent. Ancient men and women are often thought to have been primitive—physically, intellectually, linguistically, culturally and technologically, as well as morally and spiritually. The story of mankind is thought to be that of a steady upward advance in these seven spheres. Genesis, however, tells a completely different story. It presents man, not beginning as a half-ape/half-human creature and evolving into modern men and women, but as part of God's perfect creation; a creature who was perfect physically, intellectually, linguistically, culturally, technologically, morally and spiritually. The Bible presents the human race, not evolving upwards, but sinning against God and morally, physically and spiritually destitute—alienated from God. The Bible teaches very clearly that the only way for fallen men and women to be reconciled to God is in and through the death and resurrection of the Lord Jesus Christ, God's only begotten Son, who said, 'I am the way, the truth, and the life. No one comes to the Father except through Me' (John 14:6).

The biblical view of origins

Theistic evolutionists, with their evolutionary views about origins, have to rely on the ideas of evolutionists rather than on the biblical accounts for the answers to the questions of origins. Often these ideas are in direct contradiction to what the Bible teaches, in spite of the fact that many theistic evolutionists argue that they believe the Bible but simply reinterpret it in terms of evolution. But what we believe is a matter of *authority*. Who is right: God or the evolutionists? What do we believe: the Word of God or the words of evolutionists in their textbooks?

Before the first act of creation, nothing of the physical realm existed—there was only God, who is spirit. The very first act was, therefore, to create matter—'In the beginning God created the heavens and the earth' (Gen. 1:1). As soon as God created matter, he created time, because, as we have already seen, many of the properties of matter can only be explained in terms of time. Hence the Bible gives an account not only of the *origin of matter*, but also of the *origin of time*—'the beginning' is time zero, at which God began to create. The first chapter of Genesis teaches the *order of creation*; we have already seen that there are twenty-three contradictions concerning this order compared with that taught by evolutionists. Another example of how the ideas of evolutionists (whether theistic or otherwise) and the biblical accounts are in opposition to each other concerns the *origin of species*. Evolution maintains that, millions of years ago, inorganic matter acted upon by natural processes gave rise to one or more self-replicating organisms. Over time, these organisms are supposed to have evolved into all the plants and animals that we find on earth today, as well as those found fossilized in the sedimentary rocks. Evolution teaches that the origin of species is the product of chance, natural selection, time and death—a combination of Lady Luck and Father Time, as I once heard someone say. The Bible, on the other hand, teaches that on the third creation day, God created all the basic kinds of land plants; on the fifth creation day he created all the different bird and marine animal kinds; and on the sixth creation day he created all the kinds of land animals and insects, and finally Adam and Eve, the first humans.

The contrast between the evolutionists' ideas and the creation account is great. Evolution demands that one life form evolved into another and so on—that the origin of the animal species followed the pattern of uni-cellular organisms ➔ multi-cellular organisms ➔ invertebrates ➔ fish ➔ amphibians ➔ reptiles ➔ mammals ➔ humans. The Bible, on the other hand, teaches that the distinct life forms are only variable within their *kind*.

This begs the question: What is a biblical kind? For years, creationists have argued that the varieties of dogs, including wolves, coyotes and dingoes, help us to understand what a kind is. We will look at this in detail in Chapter 8.

In addition to the origin of species, the biblical account of the creation and early history of humankind gives the answers to the origins of a number of other things that puzzle evolutionists. It is obvious from reading Genesis 2–3 that the reason why God gave people *speech* was so that we are able to communicate—talk or pray (call it what you will)—with God. Man's duty towards God is summed up in what the Lord Jesus Christ called the first and great commandment, as recorded in Matthew 22:37: 'You shall love the LORD your God with all your heart, with all your soul, and with all your mind.' Oh that everyone, everywhere, were like David, who said, 'I will bless the LORD at all times; His praise shall continually be in my mouth' (Ps. 34:1)! Not only is the *origin of speech* recorded in Genesis, the *origin of languages* is there too—see Genesis 11:1–9.

The *origin of sin* is clearly taught in Genesis 3, where we read how Adam disobeyed God by eating the fruit of the tree of the knowledge of good and evil. God had warned Adam in Genesis 2:17 that '… of the tree of the knowledge of good and evil you shall not eat, for in the day that you eat of it you shall surely die'. Paul, writing to the Christians in Rome, showed that he clearly understood death to be the result of sin: 'Therefore, just as through one man sin entered the world, and death through sin …' (Rom. 5:12); 'For the wages of sin is death' (Rom. 6:23). The great mystery of why creatures die is explained by Adam's sin. Hence the early chapters of the book of Genesis give an account of the *origin of death*.

The *origin of clothes* is also described in Genesis 3—clothes were worn because of sin. After disobeying God and eating the fruit of the tree of the knowledge of good and evil, Adam and Eve '… knew that they were naked; and they sewed fig leaves together and made themselves coverings' (Gen. 3:7). This covering for sin was not acceptable, for later in the same chapter it is recorded that '… for Adam and his wife the LORD God made tunics of skin, and clothed them' (v. 21). It is obvious that God had killed an animal as a sacrifice for sin—'without shedding of blood there is no remission'

(Heb. 9:22). This slaughtered animal provided a covering not only for Adam and Eve's sin, but also for their nakedness. This sacrifice was also a pointer to the time when the Lamb of God would be sacrificed for our sins.

Adam's sin also caused a profound effect on the eating habits of some of the animals. When God created the animals, he created them to be herbivorous—that is, plant-eating—as we can see from the command he gave first to man and then to all the other creatures in Genesis 1:29–30:

See, I have given you every herb that yields seed which is on the face of all the earth, and every tree whose fruit yields seed; to you it shall be for food. Also, to every beast of the earth, to every bird of the air, and to everything that creeps on the earth, in which there is life, I have given every green herb for food.

Now, in the sedimentary rocks that are found on the earth, many of which were laid down as a result of the Flood, we find the remains of animals that were omnivorous (they ate both plants and animals) and carnivorous (they ate other animals). How can we tell? Sometimes fossilized animals are found actually in the process of eating other animals. In other cases, fossilized animal dung (called coprolites) gives evidence of the diet of the animals—what they ate. In order to account for these types of animals that are found in the geological record of the Flood, it must be assumed that some animals became carnivorous and omnivorous after the Fall but before the Flood.

It is safe to argue, however, that most, if not all, of mankind remained faithful to God's command to be herbivorous from the Fall to the time of the Flood. After the Fall, God commanded man to 'eat the herb of the field' (Gen. 3:18), and it was not until after the Flood that God told man that he could be omnivorous: 'Every moving thing that lives shall be food for you. I have given you all things, even as the green herbs' (Gen. 9:3). The early chapters of Genesis therefore give us an account of the *origin of omnivores and carnivores*.

In fact, the early chapters of Genesis give us an account of the *origin of everything*; this is borne out by the apostle John in the first verses of his Gospel: 'In the beginning was the Word, and the Word was with God, and the Word was God. He was in the beginning with God. All things were made through Him, and without Him nothing was made that was made' (John 1:1–3).

Conclusion

It can be seen that, contrary to the views of theistic evolutionists, the early chapters of Genesis are in no way poetic, symbolic or mythical. These chapters, inspired by Almighty God, give a true, accurate and historical account of the creation and early history of the earth, and are in no way evolutionary. The historical nature of the accounts lays the foundation for the plan of redemption through the death and resurrection of the Lord Jesus Christ. The book of Genesis provides, as its name implies, answers to all the important questions of origins—questions which perplex those who do not believe what God has said in his Word.

Notes

1 Since September 2007, evolution has had to be taught as fact in all English schools in order for them to conform to the Science National Curriculum.

2 **Richard Harries,** 'Science Does not Challenge My Faith—It Strengthens It', 16 April 2006, at: guardian.co.uk.

3 'New Christian Academy Rejects Creationism as "Rubbish"', 14 July 2004, at: ekklesia.co.uk.

4 'Our Beliefs', under 'About Us', at: reasons.org.

5 **John MacArthur,** *The Battle for the Beginning* (Nashville, TN: W Publishing Group, 2001), p. 26.

6 See **Russell Grigg,** 'Should Genesis be Taken Literally?', at: creation.com. When I was CEO of AiG UK, I contacted David Watson before he died and had confirmation of the contents of this letter.

7 **Dr Milner** used the lecture as the basis of a booklet entitled *Evolution and the Bible: The Inevitable Conflict* (Sheffield: Gospel Tidings, 1971).

8 **E. J. Young,** *Studies in Genesis One* (International Library of Philosophy and Theology: Biblical & Theological Studies; Philadelphia: Presbyterian and Reformed, 1973), p. 105.

9 **Dr Terry Mortensen,** 'Evolution vs. Creation: The Order of Events Matters!', 4 April 2006, at: answersingenesis.org.

10 **Henry M. Morris,** 'The Day–Age Theory', in *Creation Research Society Quarterly*, 8/1 (June 1971), p. 72.

11 Ibid.

12 J. C. Whitcomb, *The Early Earth* (rev. edn.; Grand Rapids, MI: Baker, 1986), p. 31.

13 E. K. Victor Pearce, *Who Was Adam?* (Exeter: Paternoster, 1969), fly-leaf.

14 R. J. Berry, 'I Believe in God ... Maker of Heaven and Earth', in **Derek Burke,** (ed.), *Creation and Evolution* (Leicester: IVP, 1985), p. 99.

15 Ibid.

16 Ibid. p. 101.

17 The term 'hominid' includes the extinct australopithecines (see Chapter 9 for a detailed description of these creatures) and humans (both fossilized and living).

18 J. G. Vos, quoted in *The Bible League Quarterly* (October–December 1974), p. 284.

19 Richard Dawkins, *The Root of Evil*, Part 2, 16 January 2006, Channel 4 TV.

20 G. Richard Bozarth, 'The Meaning of Evolution', in *American Atheist*, 20 September 1979, p. 30.

Mind the gap!

We shall now consider the teaching of what is commonly referred to as the 'Gap Theory'—an idea of which Christians should be very wary. This is the theory that there is a great time gap between the first two verses of the Bible—that is, between Genesis 1:1 and Genesis 1:2. This idea, as we shall see, is not, strictly speaking, a theistic evolutionary interpretation of Genesis, although it does try to reconcile the biblical account of origins with what evolutionists teach. When the first edition of this book was published, this interpretation of Genesis seemed to be going out of fashion, so I relegated a very short consideration of the errors of the basic tenets of the Gap Theory to an appendix. Today, however, the Gap Theory seems to be gaining ground again, hence I have devoted a whole chapter to it.

Although the idea behind the Gap Theory had its origins in the writings of the Dutchman Episcopius, who lived from 1583 to 1643, it was not until 200 years later that it gradually gained acceptance after it was propagated in lectures given in the early part of the nineteenth century by the famous theologian and preacher Dr Thomas Chalmers, who was one of the founders of the Free Church of Scotland and its first moderator. The reason why Dr Chalmers accepted the Gap Theory idea was not *theological* but *geological*. By interpreting the first two verses of the Bible in such a way, Dr Chalmers felt that he could accommodate the views of the geologists of his day, who were demanding vast periods of time, while at the same time maintaining a literal interpretation of the Genesis account of creation. Dr Chalmers was, I believe, a well-meaning Christian, but I do not think that he fully understood the sinister implications of taking such a compromise position.

The Gap Theory was further elaborated in the latter part of the nineteenth century by George H. Pember in his book *Earth's Earliest Ages*, which was first published in 1884, and it was then made enormously popular by the footnotes in the *Scofield Reference Bible*, which was first published in 1909. The popularity of this theory was further enhanced by the publication in 1970 of *Without Form and Void* by Arthur C. Custance.

What does the Gap Theory teach?

It is my experience that Christians are not always sure exactly what the Gap Theory teaches, or they are unaware of the problems with this teaching. In order to rectify this, we will first of all look at what the Gap Theory basically teaches. This can be summarized as follows:

• God created the universe billions of years ago.
• The geological ages proposed by evolutionists took place over billions of years of earth's history.
• The life forms that arose during that time are now preserved in the fossil record. These fossils verify that the geological ages took place.
• These life forms found in the fossil record include pre-Adamic 'people' without any souls.
• At the end of the geological ages, Satan rebelled in heaven and many angels followed him. God then cast Satan out of heaven and down to earth. By way of judgement, the earth underwent a huge cataclysmic flood (often referred to as 'Lucifer's Flood'). As a result, the earth was left without form and void, with darkness on the face of the deep, as described in Genesis 1:2.
• God then recreated the earth in the six literal days of creation (or re-creation) described in Genesis 1:3–31.

The Gap Theory gets acceptance because, on the face of it, it seems to offer rather impressive biblical support for a position that does not radically challenge the evolutionary geological timetable. However, with the advent of the modern creationist movement, especially with groups such as the Creation Research Society, the Institute for Creation Research, Answers in Genesis, the Creation Science Movement (formerly the Evolution Protest Movement) and many others, support for this compromise position has come under more scrutiny, and its interpretation of the Genesis account has been shown to be weak. Both scientific and theological scholars have shown that, not only is the Gap Theory unnecessary (because it is possible to believe the Bible's young-earth position), but it is also theologically unsound. Two books which have helped put nails in the coffin of the Gap Theory are *Unformed and Unfilled* by Weston W. Fields,[1] which was published in 1976 and *The Genesis 'Gap Theory'* by M. W. J. Phelan, which was published in 2005.[2] With these books as our guide, and with the help of what others have written, let us look more closely at the Gap Theory and compare its teachings with those of Scripture.

Problems with the Gap Theory

There are a number of problems with the Gap Theory. The first major one is the idea that the geological ages took place between Genesis 1:1 and 1:2, which is plainly proved false by what God said in the fourth commandment: 'For in six days the LORD made the heavens and the earth, the sea, and all that is in them' (Exod. 20:11). Here God is telling mankind that the pattern he set at creation (of six days of work followed by a day of rest) is to be the pattern for our working week. It needs to be noted that Exodus 20:11 covers both Genesis 1:1 *and* 1:2. In six days God made 'the heavens and the earth' (Gen. 1:1) and '... the sea, and all that is in them' (Gen. 1:2 onwards). There is no room for a gap between Genesis 1:1 and 1:2 because the statement in Exodus 20:11 covers what God did in Genesis 1:1 and in the verses after it ... and he did all this *in the six days—without any gaps!*

Another problem for those who support the Gap Theory is the fact that the Bible clearly teaches that there was no sin, death, disease or suffering in the world until Adam disobeyed God by eating the forbidden fruit—the fruit of the tree of the knowledge of good and evil. The Gap Theory, however, would have us believe that there were billions of years of death, disease and suffering, and that this is represented by the fossils and rock layers in the earth's crust, which are supposed to identify the geological ages.

A further problem for the proponents of the Gap Theory is the fact that the Gap Theory proposes that, at the end of the geological ages, Satan sinned and, as a result, was cast down to earth, and that there was then a great cataclysm. This would mean that the geological ages with countless deaths recorded in them (in the fossil record) must have occurred *before* either Satan was cast out of heaven or humans sinned. This is contrary to what the Bible clearly teaches about death being the result of Adam's sin.

These are just a few of the problems with the Gap Theory, which is another compromise position taken by those who either do not understand the implications of the idea of putting a gap between the first two verses of Scripture, or do not understand what the Bible clearly teaches about origins.

The Gap Theory is both unscientific and unscriptural, as Dr John Whitcomb has pointed out: 'Nevertheless, this theory, on closer inspection, compromises the unity and completeness of the creation account, the original perfection of the world, the genetic continuity of fossil and living forms, the totality of Adam's dominion, and the uniqueness of both the Edenic Curse and the global catastrophism of Noah's Flood.'[3] We have already seen that the Gap Theory compromises the unity and completeness of the Genesis account of the creation, and that it also compromises the teaching of the original perfection of the created world. Let us now take up the other four points made by Dr Whitcomb to elaborate further the problems of accepting this compromise position: the genetic continuity of fossil and living forms; Adam's dominion; the Edenic curse; and the Flood in the days of Noah.

The point about the genetic continuity of fossil and living forms is very interesting. The Gap Theory maintains that all the animals and plants in the original created world were destroyed and fossilized, so they should have no genetic relationship with the living things on the present 'recreated' earth. Yet many of the plants and animals on the earth today are identical in form with those found in the fossil record. Indeed, some animals are referred to as 'living fossils' because they are identical with those found in the fossil record. The coelacanth fish is probably the most famous example, although other examples abound.

One example of so-called living fossils that gives rise to a problem of epic proportions is the existence of humans found fossilized in the fossil record—Cro-Magnon Man is probably the best example. From drawings these humans made of one another, we can see that they looked identical to modern humans living today.[4] Furthermore, their skeletal remains show that they were the same as modern human beings—*Homo sapiens sapiens*. This means that humans can therefore also be called living fossils! Those who accept the Gap Theory have to believe that people like Cro-Magnon Man were pre-Adamic and were part of the world that was destroyed by 'Lucifer's flood'. They have to believe that such people did not possess an eternal soul because they were not descended from Adam. They also have to believe that these pre-Adamic people did not die because of Adam's sin—something which is clearly taught in the Bible. Furthermore, they have to believe that such people were not made in the image and likeness of God. Finally, they also have to believe that these people died before sin entered the world via Adam—something incompatible with the clear teachings of Scripture.

The second point mentioned by Dr Whitcomb is that of Adam's dominion. If the Gap Theory is correct, then, when Adam was created, he would have been a very late arrival on the scene and would have been placed on a world that had just been destroyed and recreated. He would have been walking upon a literal graveyard of billions of creatures over which he had never, nor would ever, exercise dominion, in spite of what Genesis 1:26 teaches about humans having dominion over all the creatures of the earth. Furthermore, the Gap Theory has to define the 'very good' of Genesis 1:31, for, according to this theory, when Adam was created, this 'very good' world would already have become the domain of a fallen and wicked being (Satan), who is described in Scripture as 'the god of this world' (2 Cor. 4:4, KJV).

The third point raised by Dr Whitcomb is the Edenic curse. The Gap Theory seriously undermines the doctrine of the curse which God placed upon the earth as a result of Adam's rebellion. According to the Gap Theory, animals were living and dying, not only before the Fall of Adam, but also before Satan's rebellion against God. Furthermore, some of these animals were carnivorous and others were omnivorous. In other words, they were already eating one another! This is contrary to what the Bible teaches; Scripture says that the 'groaning and travailing in pain' of the *whole* creation described in Romans 8:22 [KJV] is the result of the Edenic curse which came *after* Adam's fall. It was not until the first man deliberately rejected the revealed command of God that death made its first appearance on this planet (Rom. 5:12) and that animals fell under the 'bondage of corruption' (Rom. 8:21).

The fourth and final point raised by Dr Whitcomb about the Gap Theory is that this teaching tacitly assumes that Noah's Flood, to which the writer of the book of Genesis allocates three whole chapters, was an insignificant event from a geological point of view because 'Lucifer's flood' (which supposedly took place at some point in the gap between Genesis 1:1 and 1:2) was the cause of the formation of all the fossil-bearing sedimentary rocks. Hence the Gap Theory teaches that, far from being a global catastrophic flood, Noah's Flood was a localized event—something that is not taught either in the book of Genesis nor in the passages of the New Testament that refer to this cataclysmic event.

Does the Hebrew teach the Gap Theory?

In spite of all the arguments outlined above, some still maintain that there is a gap between Genesis 1:1 and 1:2, arguing that the Hebrew grammar and the use of Hebrew words in Genesis 1 and elsewhere in the Old Testament insist upon it. But they do not! In *Unformed and Unfilled*, Weston W. Fields accomplishes the superb task of showing that every argument used by the proponents of the Gap Theory is wrong. For example, he has shown that the grammar of Genesis 1:2 indicates 'that the clauses of which it is composed are a description of the action of the main verb (namely the action of creating the heaven and the earth in Genesis 1:1), *not a chronological sequential development after 1:1*'.[5] This same conclusion is reinforced by M. W. J. Phelan: 'The grammatical facts of Genesis 1:2 drive us to conclude that the earth was *created* in a condition the Scriptures describe as *unformed and unfilled*. The Gap Theory contradicts these plain facts, and consequently, contradicts Scripture!'[6]

Some argue that the Hebrew word *hayeta* that is translated 'was' in Genesis 1:2 should be translated 'became'. But, again, this is not so. Weston W. Fields has shown that 'was' is the traditional and only legitimate translation of *hayeta*.[7] This conclusion has also been deduced by M. W. J. Phelan[8] and this, on its own, negates one of the forceful arguments of the Gap Theory.

Weston W. Fields also examines the meanings of the two Hebrew words *asa* (to make) and *bara* (to create) and the relationships between them. He concludes that the meaning of these two words is such that 'it allows no time for a gap between Genesis 1:1 and 1:2; it allows for no gap *before* Genesis 1; and it requires *recent creation*. Only intimidation by contemporary scientism can drive one to persist in rejecting the plain teaching of Scripture.'[9] The phrase 'without form and void' has also been examined by Weston W. Fields; he has concluded 'that neither lexical definition, nor contextual usages require that we view Genesis 1:2 as a scene of judgment—an evil state created by the fall of angels'. He goes on to say that *tohu* and *bohu* are used to describe 'something unfinished, and confused, but not necessary evil!'.[10]

Finally, other arguments used by those propagating the Gap Theory have also been critically examined by Weston W. Fields. These include the following:

- That as God is the God of light, God's original creation would not have included the darkness in Genesis 1:2. Hence darkness must be evil, the result of judgement.
- That 2 Corinthians 4:6 ('For it is the God who commanded light to shine out of darkness, who has shone in our hearts to give the light of the knowledge of the glory of God in the face of Jesus Christ') supports the Gap Theory.
- That Hebrews 11:3 ('By faith we understand that the worlds were framed by the word of God, so that the things which are seen were not made of things which are visible') supports the Gap Theory, because the word translated 'framed' can also be translated 'restored'.
- The existence of fossils including those of pre-Adamic 'people'.
- The arguments in favour of 'Lucifer's flood'.

In each case, the arguments used by proponents of the Gap Theory are shown to be 'sterile, based on theological biases and extraordinarily strained'.[11]

Finally, in his book *Creation and Change*, Dr Douglas Kelly, Professor of Systematic Theology at Reformed Theological Seminary in Charlotte, North Carolina, makes the following pertinent comment about the Gap Theory: 'The "gap" theory should serve as a model of what Christians should *not* do in their legitimate desire to speak Biblical truth into a world held in the tight grip of humanistic premises.'[12] This is sound advice, not only to those who believe in the Gap Theory, but also to those who believe in theistic evolution and other compromise positions.

Conclusion

The Gap Theory, then, is a compromise formulated in the last couple of centuries in an attempt to harmonize the plain teachings of the Scriptures with the ideas of the evolutionists. In order to arrive at such a compromise position, advocates of the Gap Theory accept what evolutionists teach about millions of years and then reinterpret the Scriptures in order to make them fit in with these evolutionary ideas. The Gap Theory does not, therefore, rest upon the impregnable rock of Holy Scripture, but is founded on the shifting sands of the ideas of evolutionists.

Notes

1 **Weston W. Fields,** *Unformed and Unfilled* (Nutley, NJ: Presbyterian and Reformed, 1976).

2 **M. W. J. Phelan,** *The Genesis 'Gap Theory'* (Waterlooville: Twoedged Sword Publications, 2005)

3 **J. C. Whitcomb,** *The Early Earth* (rev. edn.; Grand Rapids, MI: Baker, 1986), p. 158.

4 See 'Those Sophisticated Cave Men', at: http://s8int.com/sophis2.html.

5 **Fields,** *Unformed and Unfilled,* pp. 75–86.

6 **Phelan,** *The Genesis 'Gap Theory',* p. 51.

7 **Fields,** *Unformed and Unfilled,* pp. 87–112.

8 **Phelan,** *The Genesis 'Gap Theory',* p. 61.

9 **Fields,** *Unformed and Unfilled,* p. 74.

10 Ibid. p. 129.

11 Ibid.

12 **Douglas F. Kelly,** *Creation and Change* (Fearn: Mentor, 1997), p. 95.

The age of the earth: biblical considerations

One of the most important questions in the creation/evolution debate concerns the age of the earth. The Bible teaches very clearly that the earth was created by Almighty God between 6,000 and 10,000 years ago. This, however, is dismissed as 'rubbish' by evolutionists. This is because evolutionists maintain that the earth is the result of the evolution of the universe and that it came into existence about 4,600 million years ago. Evolutionists argue that their date for the age of the earth is based on science whereas the creationists' date is based on faith.

In this chapter we will look carefully at what the Bible teaches about the age of the earth. In the next chapter we will investigate the methods by which evolutionists arrive at their age of the earth, to see whether these methods are accurate or not. We will look carefully at how rocks are dated and at the assumptions that are made in their age determinations. We will also look to see if there is any scientific evidence for believing that the age of the earth should be measured in thousands rather than thousands of millions of years.

Did God create everything in 4004 BC?

Did God create everything in 4004 BC—the date that is found printed in the margins of old Bibles alongside Genesis 1 and which seems to be ingrained in so many people's minds? What exactly, if anything, does the Bible teach about the age of the earth? Is it possible to arrive at an exact date for the creation of the earth? Many believe that the Bible teaches that the creation did indeed take place in 4004 BC. Although it is generally known that this is Ussher's date, many do not know who Ussher was, how he obtained this date, and how it found its way into the margin of the first page of so many Bibles.

In 1650, James Ussher, Archbishop of Armagh and Primate of Ireland, devised, by using the Bible, a system of chronology that dated creation to the evening preceding 23 October 4004 BC.[1] This date is some seventy-six years earlier than that proposed by the distinguished Greek scholar John Lightfoot, who was Vice-Chancellor of the University of Cambridge in 1644. From textual considerations, he concluded that the creation began at nine o'clock on the morning of 17 September 3929 BC. Ussher's date of 4004 BC was inserted into the margin alongside Genesis 1 in the Great (1701) Edition of the English Bible by William Lloyd, Bishop of Winchester. This practice was followed in subsequent editions. In 1900, however, Cambridge University Press stopped printing this date in their Bibles, and they were followed by Oxford University Press some ten years later.

On the face of it, calculating the age of the earth from the Bible is simplicity itself. First of all, the date of Abraham's birth must be determined. Then, by using the genealogies in Genesis 11 and 5, it should be possible to calculate when Noah and Adam lived, respectively. Finally, a consideration of Genesis 1 to determine the length of the creation days should make it possible to calculate the age of the earth. But it is not actually as straightforward as this, and there are many pitfalls and difficulties, as we shall see.

Determining the age of the earth from the Bible

The first problem is to determine when Abraham lived. At present, Abraham is known only from biblical sources, although most scholars place Abraham 'toward the beginning of the Middle Bronze Age (1900–1800 BC) or the end of the Early Bronze Age (2150–2000 BC)'.[2] An Early Bronze Age date, however, fits perfectly with the dates for Abraham that we can determine from the Bible.

Dr Edwin Thiele has produced a chronology of the kings of Israel and Judah based on information given in the books of Kings and Chronicles.[3] He has shown how these dates tie in with those given in the writings of the Assyrians and Babylonians, and also how they connect with other historical writings of the time. Furthermore, he has shown that we can know that these dates are accurate because they can be double-checked against the records of astronomical events, which are fixed.

Dr Edwin Thiele has determined that the division of the kingdom of Israel at the death of Solomon occurred in 931 BC.[4] Using this date and the time periods given in 1 Kings 6:1 and Exodus 12:40, it can be shown that Jacob must have entered Egypt in 1877 BC; since he was 130 years old at the time (Gen. 47:9), he must have been born in 2007 BC. As Isaac was sixty years old when Jacob was born (Gen. 25:26), and Abraham was one hundred years old when Isaac was born (Gen. 21:5), Abraham (or Abram, as he was known at first) must have been born in 2167 BC. This date fits perfectly with an Early Bronze Age date for Abraham as suggested by scholars.

Assuming that the genealogies in Genesis 5 and 11 are complete, and that there are father–son relationships between those named in the genealogies, we can construct the chronology shown in Table 2. This chronology shows that the Flood must have occurred in 2459 BC, some 1656 years after Adam, who would have been created in 4115 BC.

Are there gaps in biblical genealogies?

The crucial question is: Are the genealogies that are recorded in Genesis 5 and 11 complete? In other words, do they have to be interpreted as a strict chronology? The simple answer to this question is that there is no way of knowing. Some have argued that these genealogies are complete,[5] others, myself included, have argued that they *may not* be complete and that there may be gaps in them.[6] However, even if it is accepted that there are gaps in these genealogies, there are limits to how much these genealogies can be stretched.

There are twenty names in the patriarchal list from Adam to Abraham. There is a definite father–son relationship between five of these pairs: Adam and Seth (Gen. 5:3); Lamech and Noah (Gen. 5:28–30); Noah and Shem (Gen. 9:18); Shem and Arphaxad (Gen. 11:10); and Terah and Abraham (Gen. 11:26–32). Hence there are only fourteen possible generation gaps in the genealogies. If there are gaps in these genealogies, they cannot be huge. If each gap was a thousand years, for example,[7] then the date of Adam's creation would be about 18000 BC. This would mean, though, that when the genealogy records, for example, that 'Enoch lived sixty-five years, and begot Methuselah' (Gen. 5:21), we have to interpret this as meaning, 'Enoch lived sixty-five years and begot a son whose descendant 1,000 years later was Methuselah'. It has to be admitted that if

Table 2: Chronology from Adam to Abraham, assuming that there are no gaps in the genealogies given in Genesis chapters 5 and 11

Name of patriarch	Year of birth		Age at birth of next patriarch	Year of death
	AC	BC		AC
Adam	–	4115	130	930
Seth	130	3985	105	1042
Enosh	235	3880	90	1140
Cainan	325	3790	70	1235
Mahalaleel	395	3720	65	1290
Jared	460	3655	162	1422
Enoch	622	3493	65	987[a]
Methuselah	687	3428	187	1656
Lemach	874	3241	182	1651
Noah	1056	3059	502[b]	2006
Shem	1558[b]	2561[b]	100[b]	2158[c]
Arphaxad	1658[b]	2457	35	2096[c]
Salah	1693	2422	30	2126[c]
Eber	1723	2392	34	2187[c]
Peleg	1757	2358	30	1996[c]
Reu	1787	2328	32	2026[c]
Serug	1819	2296	30	2049[c]
Nahor	1849	2266	29	1997[c]
Terah	1878	2237	70	2083
Abram	1948	2167	100	2123

AC After Creation (or Adam)

BC Before Christ

(a) 'By faith Enoch was taken away so that he did not see death, "and was not found, because God had taken him"' (Heb. 11:5).

(b) The Flood occurred in 1656 AC (when Noah was 600 years old) and Genesis 11:10 records that Shem was 100 years old when he begat Arphaxad, two years after the Flood.

(c) These dates may not be the year of death.

this was done for the fourteen possible gaps, it would stretch the genealogies to almost breaking point.

However, we do have a clear example of a gap in a genealogy given in the Scriptures in Matthew 1:8, where we read that 'Joram begot Uzziah'. When we turn to the historical books of the Old Testament, however, we discover that Joram (also known as Jehoram) was the father of Ahaziah (2 Chr. 22:1); Ahaziah was the father of Joash (2 Chr. 22:11); Joash was the father of Amaziah (2 Chr. 24:27); and Amaziah was the father of Uzziah (also known as Azariah; 2 Chr. 26:1). So instead of the genealogy being Joram–Uzziah, it was in fact Joram–Ahaziah–Joash–Amaziah–Uzziah. Three generations have been omitted, and this amounts to seventy-four years.

Although we do not know for certain whether there are any gaps in the genealogies in Genesis 5 and 11, we can be certain that, if there are any, they are not huge. We can be confident, therefore, that although we may not be able to date the creation of Adam exactly, it is doubtful whether it could have been much earlier than 4004 BC. However, it is not possible to go as far as determining the month or the exact day of the month, as others have done.

The Bible teaches that Adam was created on the sixth day of creation, and we have seen that the days in Genesis 1 are literal, historical days and that there is no gap between Genesis 1:1 and 1:2. This means that the date of the creation of the earth is essentially the same as the date of Adam's creation, for he was created only six days after the creation of the earth. This means that the earth is not much older than 6,000 years. The conclusion at which we arrive as we consider what the Bible teaches about the age of the earth is therefore very clear. Although we may not be able to calculate the *exact* age of the earth from the Bible, we are absolutely certain that its age should be measured in thousands, not thousands of millions, of years.

Superficial appearance of age

Having established that the creation took place a mere few thousand years ago, it is important to realize that God gave everything that he had made a superficial appearance of age. It is important to understand exactly what this means, and even more important to understand its significance. Before embarking on a geochronologist's excursion into the Garden of Eden, however, it is useful to consider one or two of the miracles that our Lord Jesus Christ performed during his earthly ministry. This will give us a much better understanding of what we mean by 'superficial appearance of age'.

The account of Jesus's *first* miracle is found in John 2. Jesus was at a wedding in Cana of Galilee and, at the wedding reception, he turned water into wine.[8] Now the difference between water and wine is considerable— you only have to taste them both to confirm this! Water is a relatively simple substance, with the chemical formula H_2O. Wine, on the other hand, is an exceedingly complex solution containing a great number of complex organic compounds (alcohols, esters, fatty acids, pigments, etc.). One could argue that, in nature, water in soil is changed into wine by the natural processes involved in the formation of grapes and their fermentation to produce wine. The water in the soil is absorbed by the root of the vine and is eventually turned into grape juice in the grape as the fruit ripens. The juice is squeezed out of the grape and is fermented by yeast until all the sugars in it have been converted into alcohol. Acids and esters are also produced. After fermentation has ceased, the wine has to mature for several months before it is palatable. The chemistry of maturation is complex. Hence the natural process of transforming water into wine is complex and takes several months—sometimes years.

The Lord Jesus Christ, however, accomplished the transformation of water into wine instantaneously and without the use of grapes or the fermentation process. When the wine was only a few minutes old, it had a superficial appearance of age, for it appeared to be several months, if not years, old. We can see this by the reaction of the guests recorded in John 2:10. The master of the wedding feast thought that it was ordinary (although good) wine which the host had kept back until that point. He thought that it was the end product of the natural fermentation and maturation processes of the fruit of the vine—he could not tell the difference between this created wine and ordinary, naturally produced wine.

The notion of superficial appearance of age is again illustrated in the miracle of the feeding of the five thousand that is recorded in Luke 9. Dr John Whitcomb, commenting on this miracle, points out,

One evening on a mountainside near the Sea of Galilee, five thousand men and their families ate loaves and fishes that were created with an appearance of age. Here were tens of thousands of barley loaves composed of grains that had neither been harvested from fields nor baked in ovens! And here were at least ten thousand fishes that had never hatched from eggs or been caught in nets or been dried in the sun![9]

Other miracles that Jesus Christ performed during his earthly ministry also serve to illustrate and elucidate the concept of superficial appearance of age:

- the healing of the man who had been bedridden for thirty-eight years (John 5:5–9)
- the healing of the woman who had been bent double for eighteen years (Luke 13:11–13)
- the healing of the man who was deaf and dumb (Mark 7:32–35).

In each case, the person who had been healed had organs (for example, ears that heard and a voice box that spoke, in the case of the man who had been deaf and dumb) that would have appeared to be perfectly normal organs that the person had had all his or her life. No one would have been able to detect that the new organs had been created when the person had been healed. This is because the created organs had a superficial appearance of age.

Now with this concept firmly established, let us consider the creation as recorded in Genesis 1. This, too, had a superficial appearance of age. When God commanded the earth to bring forth fruit trees, he did not create seeds first and then wait a number of years for them to grow to maturity. Some may object to this, pointing out that this is different from the way in which God produces fruit trees today. However, if we accept their line of argument, we would have to argue that God could not have created the first fruit seeds either, for these can only come from fruit trees. We cannot allow natural observation today to be our guide when we consider the supernatural creative acts of God when he first created. Similarly, all the other plant life that appeared on the third day of creation was created fully mature.

The fish that swarmed in the seas were also created fully grown on the fifth day of creation. These fish had never hatched from eggs—just like the fish in the miracle of the feeding of the five thousand men and their families. The chickens that God created on the fifth day of creation had never hatched from eggs either! The animals that appeared on the sixth day of creation were also created fully adult—so, too, were Adam and Eve.

Genesis 1 tells us no fewer than ten times that God created plants and animals to reproduce after their own kind. All these plants and animals must have been created with a superficial appearance of age. Scripture tells us that God began the biological life-cycles of these plants and animals with adult organisms. Both Old and New Testaments teach that Adam and Eve were created as adults—they were not created as helpless babes unable to fend for themselves. And this must have been true for the other creatures that God created, as Dr John Whitcomb concludes: 'And how could infant mammals have survived without a mother's care? God would have had to intervene directly and continually to care for them. Therefore, unless we appeal to an endless supply of miracles, the direct creation of *adult* organisms remains the only logical interpretation of the Genesis account of the creation of living things *after their kind.*'[10]

Now let us see how this apparent appearance of age as related to the plant and animal creation can have a significant effect on attempts to arrive at a figure for the age of the earth. Although the earth was created in a moment, it would have had the appearance of being hundreds or even thousands of years old. For example, a soil scientist trying to determine the age of the soil in the Garden of Eden would come to the conclusion that it was at least 1,000 years old, and possibly much older, for soil can take over a thousand years to form naturally.[11] Yet the soil was just a few days old!

Now, with this concept of superficial appearance of age in mind, I want us to imagine Adam in the Garden of Eden on the sixth day of creation—just after God had created Eve as a wife for him. Let us imagine that Adam wakes up and looks at Eve and concludes that she is an adult, possibly in her twenties. Feeling hungry, he takes some fruit off one of the trees, and he observes that he is in a mature garden that must have been cultivated for well over half a century, bearing in mind the mature trees and plants that are growing in it. He and Eve stroll around the Garden and walk to look at the river that flows out of the Garden. Adam observes that it is flowing in a valley which would have taken hundreds of thousands of years to have formed by the river slowly eroding the rocks. Later, Adam and Eve walk along the banks of the river Pishon and visit the land of Havilah, where they discover gold. This element is supposed to have been formed deep in the crust of the earth over a period of many millions of years. So Adam, who had been created just a few hours previously, lived in a world that appeared to be millions of years old—yet it was less than a week old.

Some may object to this doctrine of apparent age, arguing that it makes God a deceiver. God, however, has *not* deceived us—he has given us his Word to tell us what he has done. As Christian theologian and apologist Edwin John Carnell so pertinently pointed out, 'We must cheerfully admit God's moral right to create things which only appear, but are not actually, old. The limits of how God has employed this privilege must be measured—in the last analysis—not from science, but from Scripture.'[12]

Conclusion

In this chapter, we have looked at the problems of determining the age of the earth from Scripture. We have had to admit that there are difficulties in working out the exact age of the earth using the Bible because we are not absolutely certain whether or not there are gaps in the genealogies that are recorded in Genesis 5 and 11. We have also considered the problem of trying to determine the age of something when it has a superficial appearance of age—something that would have affected everything when God created it. One thing we do know for certain from the Bible, however, is that the age of the earth should be measured in terms of *thousands*, not *thousands of millions*, of years.

Notes

1 **James Ussher,** *The Annals of the World* (revised and updated by **Larry** and **Marion Pierce;** Green Forest, AR: Master Books, 2003).

2 See under 'Abraham' in **Walter A. Elwell,** (ed.), *Baker Encyclopedia of the Bible,* vol. i (Grand Rapids, MI: Baker, 1997), p. 11.

3 **Edwin R. Thiele,** *The Mysterious Numbers of the Hebrew Kings* (rev. edn.; Grand Rapids, MI: Kregel, 1994).

4 Ibid. p. 79.

5 Jonathan Sarfati, 'Biblical Chronogenealogies', at: creation.com; **Professor Dr Samuel R. Külling,** *Are the Genealogies in Genesis 5 and 11 Historical and Complete, that is, Without Gaps?* (Riehen: Immanuel-Verlag, 1996).

6 Henry Morris and **John Whitcomb,** *The Genesis Flood* (London: Evangelical Press, 1969), pp. 474–489; **A. J. Monty White,** *How Old is the Earth?* (Welwyn: Evangelical Press, 1985), pp. 21–30.

7 I have deliberately chosen a thousand years because in the New Testament, the Lord Jesus Christ was called 'the Son of David', and there were about a thousand years between the time when David lived and the time when Jesus lived.

8 John tells us that each jar held between twenty and thirty US gallons. Six jars could therefore hold anything between 120 and 180 US gallons. As there are about four litres to a US gallon, 120 to 180 US gallons is equivalent to 480 to 720 litres—that's about 640 to 960 ordinary 750 ml bottles of wine!

9 John C. Whitcomb, *The Early Earth* (rev. edn.; Grand Rapids, MI: Baker, 1986), p. 41.

10 Ibid. pp. 44–45.

11 See 'Soils Retrogression and Degradation' on Wikipedia, at: en.wikipedia.org.

12 Edwin John Carnell, quoted in **Whitcomb,** *The Early Earth*, p. 48.

Scientific dating methods

As outlined in the previous chapter, evolutionists reject the biblical arguments for the age of the earth. Using the words of Sir Charles Lyell, they argue that geology has indeed been freed from Moses[1] and that we do not have to rely on the Bible to determine the age of the earth. But does it actually matter how old the earth really is? Yes it does, for the answer that is given to this question affects our view of origins. It cannot be overemphasized that there are two irreconcilable views regarding origins: creation *or* evolution. Which one is correct? One thing is certain: if it can be shown that the earth is only a few thousand years old, evolution cannot be correct. This is because evolutionists maintain that evolution requires vast periods of time for it to occur. This factor cannot be exaggerated because it is argued that chance natural processes would have needed to operate over eons in order to bring about the origin and evolution of life on earth. Darwin was fully aware of this time factor when he declared in *On the Origin of Species* that anyone who 'does not admit how incomprehensibly vast have been the past periods of time may at once close this volume'.[2]

If we hear of a frog turning *instantaneously* into a handsome prince when kissed by a beautiful princess, we can safely assume that we are being told a fairy story. However, evolutionists think that, given enough time ('incomprehensibly vast' periods of time, according to Charles Darwin, remember), anything will, can—and even does—happen. For example, evolutionists believe that some kind of amphibian (a frog is an amphibian) has turned into a human being (and a prince is a human being!) over a period of about 350 million years. This is not regarded as a fairy tale, but as scientific fact! It seems that the enormous period of time believed to be involved deadens people's reasoning so that they believe the unbelievable and the incredible becomes credible!

What age, then, do evolutionists consider the earth to be? The answer is a staggering 4,600 million years (that's 4,600,000,000 years). We can hardly imagine such a timescale. However, if the time period were represented by, for example, *one year*, then *one second* would be equivalent to *146 years*.

On such a timescale, Martin Luther, who lived from 1483–1546, would have lived about 3.4 seconds ago; Jesus Christ's earthly ministry would have occurred a mere 13.6 seconds ago; King David, who lived around 1000 BC, would have lived 20.6 seconds ago. On the same timescale, if you accept Ussher's date of 4004 BC for Adam and Eve, they would have lived just over forty-one seconds ago!

How are rocks dated?

Before we answer this question, we have to consider how we know how old anything is. For example, how do *you* know how old *you* are? You know because of a written record—your birth certificate—which informs you of the date of your birth. Generally speaking, we know when certain events occurred in the past because of eyewitness accounts that have left us with written records. In fact, such written records are the only reliable methods of determining when events occurred, and even then we must be sure that their writers were telling the truth. But how can we date an event for which there is no written record? This is the problem that faces us when we try to determine the age of the earth without using the written record contained in the early chapters of Genesis.

Some of the earliest attempts to determine the age of the earth using only scientific methods were made during the eighteenth century. Such determinations ignored the Bible's evidence about our living on an earth which is only a few thousand years old. One of these methods was to determine the time it would take for various salts in the ocean to build up to their present concentrations based on present-day rates of accumulation; thus the amount of any given chemical in the ocean was divided by the annual increment, via river flow, of that chemical. Such a simple age determination of the earth assumes that the particular chemical was not present in the ocean to begin with and that its rate of inflow has always been the same. It also assumes that the particular chemical is not being precipitated out anywhere or being recycled in any way.

Because there are so many different chemicals in the ocean, many different calculations can be made in this way. Interestingly, they all give different answers, as can be seen in Table 3, which lists the times taken for twelve different elements to accumulate to their present concentrations in

Table 3: Times taken for various elements to accumulate to their present concentrations in the ocean via river inflow

Chemical element	Years to accumulate
Sodium	260 million
Magnesium	45 million
Silicon	8,000
Potassium	11 million
Copper	50,000
Gold	560,000
Silver	2.1 million
Mercury	42,000
Lead	2,000
Tin	100,000
Nickel	18,000
Uranium	500,000

the ocean via river inflow.[3] The reason why different times are obtained is because an unknown amount of each element was present in the ocean to start with. Also, in some cases, some mechanism for recycling *may* exist to return a proportion of that element back to the continents for transportation to the ocean again.

As we can see, such a relatively 'simple' scientific dating method does not give us the age of the earth. The real problem is, how can we date a rock? For example, when were the rock strata upon which your house is built laid down? How can we really know the answer to such a question if no one was there to observe these rock strata being deposited and to record it for posterity?

It is particularly interesting to look at the type of information that is *not* used in order to date a rock. By doing so, we shall remove some popular misconceptions about what data is used to date rocks. Although I have gleaned much of this information from a book that was published in 1974,[4] it is as relevant to the study of geochronology (the measurement of the ages of rocks and geological events) today as it was when it was first published.

We learn that rocks are not dated by their physical appearance, by their petrological character (that is, their overall structure and composition), by their mineralogical content or by their structural features. Furthermore, they are not dated by vertical superposition—that is, the order in which rocks lie on one another—or by the rocks adjacent to them. In other words, they are not dated by any physical characteristics at all. Surprisingly, rocks are not dated using radiometric dating (see below) or by their *total* fossil content. How, then, *are* rocks dated?

The answer to this question is that a rock is dated by its *index fossil*. Index fossils are the fossilized remains of organisms, usually marine invertebrates, that are assumed to have been widespread geographically but with a rather limited duration chronologically. Hence their presence in any rock is supposed to date that rock unambiguously. But this begs the question: How does the geochronologist (the scientist who determines the ages of rocks) know how old the *index fossil* is? The answer to this question is 'Evolution'. But this is circular reasoning:

- Rocks are dated by index fossils, the ages of which are determined by evolution.
- But the proof of evolution is the age of the rocks in which the fossils are found.

Hence the basis of dating rocks is evolution, and the only proof of evolution is the ages of the rocks in which the fossils are found. The main evidence for evolution is the assumption of evolution! Hence fossils really cannot provide a satisfactory method for dating rocks. There is, therefore, no *proof* from sedimentary rocks that the vast evolutionary timescale is valid.

Radiometric dating

In the next three sections, we shall be considering how rocks are dated using radiometric dating (including radiocarbon dating) and tree-ring dating. Some of the material in these sections is, by its very nature, technical. If you find these sections hard going, skip them and continue reading at the section 'Scientific evidence for a young earth'.

Radiometric dating is one method that is favoured by geochronologists to determine the ages of rocks. The method relies on the fact that certain isotopes (or kinds) of certain elements are radioactive. These isotopes, which are called radio-isotopes, are unstable and decay into other elements, which are often called 'daughter elements'. For example, the isotope of the element uranium that is called uranium-238 decays into an isotope of lead that is called lead-206. Radiocarbon, an isotope of carbon that is called carbon-14, decays into nitrogen-14, while potassium-40 decays either into argon-40 or into calcium-40. Sometimes the decay process is simple and involves only one step, as in the case of radiocarbon; at other times, the process is more complex with several intermediate steps, as in the case of uranium-238, which decays into lead-206 via no fewer than fourteen steps.

The principle of radiometric dating is straightforward. When molten rock, such as a lava flow, cools and solidifies, any radio-isotope that is trapped in the rock will begin to decay into its daughter element(s). By measuring the amount of the parent and daughter element(s) in the rock, and by knowing the rate at which the parent element decays into the daughter element(s), the date at which the rock formed (i.e. when it solidified) can be determined.

There are, however, a number of assumptions that are made by geochronologists, and these have a significant effect on the accuracy of such age determinations. In radiometric dating, it is *always* assumed that the *rate of decay* of the parent element into its daughter element(s) is *constant*. Students studying science in schools, colleges and universities are taught that nothing can change the rate of decay of a radio-isotope. This, however, is not true. The scientific literature contains a number of reports from scientists who have discovered that the rates of decay of radio-isotopes are not constant. For example, it has been discovered that the rate of decay of the radio-isotope beryllium-7 is pressure dependant.[5] In other words, the rate of decay changes as the pressure changes. Furthermore, it has been shown that the amount of radiation (that is, the measure of the amount of the decay) emitted from molecular monolayers (that is, single layers of atoms) of carbon with radiocarbon added, is not the same as that calculated assuming a constant radiocarbon decay rate.[6]

There is also evidence that the decay rates of uranium into lead vary with time. The first indication comes from the study of *pleochroic haloes*. When a rock crystallizes, the crystals of the minerals in the rock often enclose minute grains of other minerals which contain radioactive uranium or thorium. When the uranium or the thorium disintegrates, the *alpha* particles that are emitted are slowed down by the crystals in which the grains of the uranium- or thorium-bearing minerals are embedded. When these *alpha* particles finally stop, crystal deformation occurs, and this is shown by a discoloration or a darkening of the crystals. When the crystal is examined under a microscope, these discolorations appear as dark rings called 'pleochroic haloes'. The radius of a pleochroic halo in a particular mineral depends on the amount of energy of the *alpha* particle. This amount of energy depends on the probability of emission of the *alpha* particle which, in turn, depends on the rate of decay responsible for this *alpha*-particle emission. In other words, the size of the radius of the pleochroic halo in a particular crystal depends on the rate of the decay responsible for the *alpha*-particle emission. If it can be shown that the radii of pleochroic haloes corresponding to a definite decay in a particular mineral are of constant size, it can then be safely assumed that the rate of decay is constant. If, on the other hand, it can be shown that the radii vary, this is proof that the decay is not constant. Interestingly, it has been found that the radii of pleochroic haloes due to the radioactive decay of uranium and thorium do in fact vary in size in the *same* minerals.[7] This proves that the radioactive decay rates of these two elements are not constant, but vary over time.

More evidence that the radioactive decay rate of uranium-238 has varied in the past has come from the amount of helium found in zircon crystals trapped in granite. These zircon crystals contain radioactive uranium-238 which, over time, decays to lead-206. During the process, eight helium atoms are produced; helium, being such a light gas, migrates quickly out of the zircon crystals and the granite. However, large amounts of helium are found in the zircon crystals, suggesting that in the past, the radioactive decay was much faster than it is today.[8]

The first assumption—that the rate of decay of a parent radio-isotope into its daughter is constant—is therefore invalid. The *second* assumption in radiometric dating concerns how much of the parent and daughter elements were present in the rock when the rock formed (or, more correctly, solidified). You may think that it is assumed that there was no daughter present, but this is not often the case. For example, the age of the earth is determined by measuring the amounts of uranium and lead on the earth and then *assuming* its composition (that is, the amounts of uranium and lead present) when it formed. Some people find this unbelievable, but it is clearly stated in geology textbooks.[9] It cannot be overemphasized that *no* rock on the earth has ever been dated as being 4,600 million years old.

In the potassium–argon dating method, it is often *assumed* that some of the argon-40 in the rock came from the atmosphere when it formed (solidified). This amount is then estimated. To do this, the amount of argon-36 in the rock sample is measured. It is then assumed that the ratio of argon-36 to argon-40 in the atmosphere today has remained unchanged in the past, even though there is no proof of this. From this ratio, the amount of argon-40 in the rock when it first formed is calculated. But such a calculation is based on *two* assumptions:

- that some of the argon-40 in the rock came from the atmosphere when the rock solidified
- that the ratio of argon-36 to argon-40 in the atmosphere has remained constant.

There is no *proof* whatsoever that these two assumptions are correct; more disconcerting still is the fact that there is no way of knowing whether they are correct or not.

With the rubidium–strontium dating method, it is impossible to distinguish between the strontium-87 in the rock that has been formed by the radioactive decay of rubidium-87, and the strontium-87 that was in the rock when the rock formed. The geochronologist estimates the amount of strontium-87 that was present when the rock formed by measuring the amount of strontium-87 in the calcium plagioclase crystals (certain calcium-containing crystals) in the same rock and then assuming that this was the concentration of strontium-87 in the potassium-bearing crystals in the rock when it formed. In practice, the geochronologist measures the total amount of rubidium-87, strontium-86 and strontium-87 in each mineral in the rock mass and then draws a graph on which the ratio strontium-87 : strontium-86 is plotted against the ratio rubidium-87 : strontium-86. This graph is called an 'isochron diagram'; if all goes well (and often it does not), the date on which the rock solidified and crystallized can be calculated from the slope of the isochron that has been plotted. The intersection on the vertical axis is supposed to give the initial ratio of strontium-87 : strontium-86. The problem is that there is no way of knowing if this ratio was a constant throughout the whole rock; if it was not, the isochron is meaningless.

The *third* assumption that is made in radiometric dating is that the system has remained 'closed' since the rock formed—that no parent or daughter element(s) was added to or taken out of the rock from the time of its solidification. It is simply not possible to know whether this assumption is justified or not. With the potassium–argon dating method, for example, potassium can easily leach out of the rock by rainwater percolating through the rock, because potassium salts are soluble in water. Furthermore, the argon produced by the decay of the potassium can easily diffuse through the rock, and the rate of diffusion will depend not only upon the type of rock, but also upon its depth in the earth's crust, because pressure will affect the rate of diffusion. Both factors will cause a false age to be obtained for a rock where leaching or diffusion has occurred.

'The proof of the pudding is in the eating', as the saying goes. The proof of radiometric dating methods is therefore in their accuracy. Usually, only one radiometric method of dating can be used to determine the age of a rock, so very often no check can be made on its accuracy—unless, of course, the age of the rock is known from historical sources. Potassium–argon dating has been considered to be one of the most reliable radiometric dating methods. However, doubts have been cast on its reliability by the discovery that old ages have been obtained by this method of dating for young rocks that formed as a result of volcanic eruptions. The fact that the rocks are young is known because they were observed forming. The data in Table 4 illustrates this point adequately[10] and raises the following questions: If radiometric dating fails to give an accurate age of a rock whose true age we know from historical observation, how can it be trusted to give us the correct age for a rock whose true age we do not know from historical observation? If the methods do not work for rocks of known age, why should we trust them for rocks of unknown age?

But what about dating rocks when there is more than one method of

Table 4: Old potassium–argon dates obtained for young rocks

Volcanic eruption	When the rock formed	Date obtained by Potassium–argon dating
Mt. Etna basalt, Sicily	122 BC	170,000–330,000 years old
Mt. Etna basalt, Sicily	AD 1972	210,000–490,000 years old
Mt. St. Helens, Washington State, USA	AD 1986	Up to 2.8 million years old
Hualalai basalt, Hawaii	AD 1800–1801	1.32–1.76 million years old
Mt. Ngauruhoe, New Zealand	AD 1954	Up to 3.5 million years old
Kilauea Iki basalt, Hawaii	AD 1959	1.7–15.3 million years old

dating that can be used? Surely it is reasonable to assume that different methods of dating should give the same age. Yes, this is a reasonable expectation, but instead, what are called 'discordant ages' are often found. We will look first at an example that was published in 1971. (Not many examples are found in the more recent evolutionary scientific literature. This is because evolutionists have been wary to publish such discordant ages, realizing that creationists will seize upon them and publish them in their literature in order to show the inaccuracies of radiometric dating methods.)

Although volcanic rocks cannot be dated by their fossils (because they do not contain any), the fossils in the adjacent sedimentary rocks are often used to date them. A report was published of a basalt rock in Nigeria being dated by the fossils in the adjacent sedimentary rocks as being of 'Upper Tertiary Age'.[11] This could be anything from two to twenty-six million years old. The uranium–lead radiometric dating method dated the same rock as 750 million years old. When geologists measured the amount of helium gas in the rocks (that is, a measure of the *alpha*-particle emission) rather than the lead content, the basalt was dated as fourteen million years old. To confuse the issue further, more differing results were obtained from the potassium–argon dating method (ninety-five million years) and from fission-track measurements (less than thirty million years). The results are summarized in Table 5.

Table 5: Ages obtained for a Nigerian basalt rock

Dating method	Age obtained
Conventional Geology (based on fossils in adjacent rocks)	2–26 million years
Uranium–helium	14 million years
Fission tracks	less than 30 million years
Potassium–argon	95 million years
Uranium–lead	750 million years

Here there was a complete lack of agreement in the ages obtained for the *same* rock using different methods of dating. Which age was correct? The straightforward answer is that no one knows, for the simple reason that no one saw the basalt solidifying. Such examples show the complete unreliability of radiometric dating methods.

In 1997 a group of creationist scientists started an eight-year research project to investigate the age of the earth. The group called themselves the 'Radioisotopes and the Age of the Earth' (RATE) group. Their objective was to gather data commonly ignored or censored by those working in the field of geochronology. One area of research they undertook was to collect a rock sample and then to determine its age using different radiometric

Table 6: Beartooth Mountains sample results

Radiometric dating method	Date (millions of years)	Type of sample
Potassium–argon	1,520	Quartz–plagioclase mineral
	2,011	Whole rock
	2,403	Biotite mineral
	2,620	Hornblende mineral
Rubidium–strontium	2,515	5 minerals
	2,790	Previously published result based on 30 whole rock samples
Samarium–neodymium	2,886	4 minerals
Lead–lead	2,689	5 minerals

Table 7: Bass Rapids Sill sample results

Radiometric dating method	Date (millions of years)	Type of sample
Potassium–argon	841.5	11 whole rock samples
	665–1,053	Model ages from single whole rocks
Rubidium–strontium	1,007	Magnetite mineral grains from 7 rock samples
	1,055	11 whole rock
	1,060	7 minerals
	1,070	Previously published age based on 5 whole rock samples
	1,075	12 minerals
Lead–lead	1,250	11 whole rock
	1,327	6 minerals
Samarium–neodymium	1,330	8 minerals
	1,336	Magnetite mineral grains from 7 rock samples
	1,379	6 minerals

dating methods. If the different radiometric dating methods are accurate, they should give the *same* age for the rock.

Two of the sites from which they took rock samples have been dated by evolutionary geologists as being from the so-called pre-Cambrian period—that is, older than 543 million years. Rock samples were taken from the Beartooth Mountains of north-west Wyoming near Yellowstone National Park and from the Bass Rapids Sill in the central part of Arizona's Grand Canyon, USA. All the samples (whole rock and separate minerals within the rock) were analysed using four different radiometric dating methods—potassium–argon, rubidium–strontium, samarium–neodymium and lead–lead. In order to avoid any criticism of bias, the analyses were contracted out to commercial laboratories located in Colorado and Massachusetts in the USA and in Ontario in Canada.

Tables 6 and 7 show the results for the radiometric age determinations for the rocks from the Beartooth Mountains and the Bass Rapids Sill, Grand Canyon, respectively.[12] Evolutionary geologists believe that the rocks in the Beartooth Mountains are some of the oldest in the USA and that they are 2,790 million years old. Yet, as can be seen from Table 6, the radiometric dates obtained by the RATE group using four different radiometric dating methods show a scatter ranging from 1,520 to 2,886 million years, and the difference in the results obtained using potassium–argon dating amount to a staggering 1,100 million years! Evolutionary geologists believe that the age of the rocks in the Bass Rapids Sill in the Grand Canyon is 1,070 million years. Table 7 shows, however, that the radiometric dates for these rocks give ages ranging from 665 to 1,379 million years—a difference of 714 million years! Such data shows the complete inaccuracy and unreliability of radiometric dating.

We have seen that radiometric dating is based on the assumption that the decay rate of a radio-isotope is constant, even though there is experimental evidence that in one or two cases this is not so. It is also based on assumptions regarding the initial conditions which are not always known. Furthermore, it is based on the assumption that the system is closed, even though very often we simply do not know whether this is so or not. Because of the problems with these assumptions, we should expect radiometric dating to be unreliable. And this is what we discover. Potassium–argon dating, for example, is notoriously inaccurate and gives ages of millions of years for lavas that are known from written sources to be less than 200 years old. Different radiometric dating methods usually give different ages for the same rock, although occasionally concordant ages are obtained. These occasions when ages agree should not, however, be used as proof that radiometric dating is accurate and that the earth is therefore 4,600 million years old. Yet, in spite of all this, many people have been led to believe that they can trust radiometric dating, especially radiocarbon dating.

Radiocarbon dating

Radiocarbon dating has obtained widespread use in archaeology and geology. Most people that I meet seem to think that radiocarbon dating can be used to date anything and that it has been used to prove that the earth is millions of years old. This method of dating, however, can only be used to estimate the age of materials of *biological* origin (e.g. bones, teeth, wood and so on), and even then, if it were accurate, it could only be used to date materials that are less than 50,000 years old.

This method of dating was developed in the mid-1940s at the University of Chicago by Professor Willard F. Libby, who was subsequently awarded the Nobel Prize in Chemistry in 1960 for this work. In this section we will look at the principles upon which radiocarbon dating is based, the assumptions inherent in this method of dating, and the extent to which the dates obtained by this method have been checked against accurate historically dated materials.

The basic theory behind radiocarbon dating is that, in the upper atmosphere of the earth, nitrogen is changed into a rare form of carbon, known as radiocarbon, due to its reaction with atomic particles called neutrons.[13] These neutrons are produced as a result of the bombardment of the upper atmosphere by cosmic rays. The nitrogen–neutron reaction produces not only radiocarbon but also protons.

'Ordinary' carbon is carbon-12 that has six protons and six neutrons in its atomic nucleus. Radiocarbon is a different isotope (or kind) of carbon and is also known as carbon-14. Radiocarbon has the same number of protons in its atomic nucleus as carbon-12—that is, six—but it has two extra neutrons, making a total of eight. Unlike carbon-12, radiocarbon is radioactive and disintegrates back into nitrogen with the emission of an electron. This disintegration process is relatively slow. Radiocarbon is said to have a half-life of 5,730 years. This means that, starting with one gram of radiocarbon, after 5,730 years one half of it will have disintegrated into nitrogen and half a gram of radiocarbon will be left. After a further 5,730 years, half of this half-gram will have disintegrated and only a quarter of a gram of radiocarbon will be left. After another equally long period of time, only an eighth of a gram of radiocarbon will be left, and so on.

Since the newly formed radiocarbon in the atmosphere has the same chemical properties as ordinary carbon, it can and does combine with the oxygen in the air to form carbon dioxide. This carbon dioxide diffuses through the atmosphere and is thought to be distributed evenly in the atmosphere and subsequently in the oceans. The amount of radiocarbon in the carbon dioxide of our present atmosphere is very low. There is, on average, only *one* carbon atom with the atomic weight of 14 for every

1,000,000,000,000 (that's one trillion) with the atomic weight of 12. This ratio, $1 : 10^{12}$, has been determined because, as the radiocarbon disintegrates, it emits an electron that is detected using very sensitive equipment.

The carbon dioxide, with its radiocarbon component, is assimilated by plants during photosynthesis, and finally also by animals, which ultimately live on plants. Hence at any given time, the ratio between active and non-active carbon in *all* living organisms is essentially the same as that in the air—that is, $1 : 10^{12}$. Now, when an organism dies, it is unable to take up further radiocarbon, and that which is already present diminishes due to radioactive decay. Because the activity of the radiocarbon in a sample (measured by detecting the electron emission of the radiocarbon as it decays into nitrogen) decreases at what is assumed to be a constant rate, it is possible, by measuring the present activity of the sample, to determine the time elapsed since death occurred. Providing that *all* the assumptions inherent in the method are valid, the technique may be applied to samples which are between 100 and 50,000 years old.

This method is, no doubt, very ingenious and powerful, providing that *all* the following six assumptions are valid:[14]

1. that the amount of cosmic radiation—and hence the amount of neutron bombardment in the upper atmosphere—has been essentially constant over the last 50,000 years
2. that the concentration of radiocarbon in the carbon dioxide of the atmosphere has been constant over the last 50,000 years
3. that the carbon dioxide content of the ocean and atmosphere has been constant over the same period of time
4. that dead organic matter is not later altered with respect to its carbon content by any biological or other activity
5. that the rate of decay of radiocarbon is constant
6. that the rate of formation of radiocarbon in the upper atmosphere and its rate of disappearance from the biosphere are in equilibrium and have been so during the last 50,000 years.

These six assumptions, *all* of which must be valid if radiocarbon dating is to be accurate, must be critically examined from a scientific viewpoint.

The first three assumptions are contrary to some of the arguments advanced as causes of the Ice Age(s). Of the several hypotheses which have been advanced by geologists to account for the onset of the Ice Age(s), the ones most favoured by them are:[15]

- variation in the sun's radiation
- an increase in the amount of carbon dioxide present in the atmosphere.

If the first hypothesis is correct, then assumption 1 is not true and assumption 2 is therefore also invalid. This is because the ratio of radiocarbon to ordinary carbon depends on how many neutrons bombard the upper atmosphere and that, in turn, depends on the amount or intensity of cosmic radiation. If, on the other hand, the second hypothesis is correct, assumption 3 is untrue because the carbon dioxide content of the atmosphere, and subsequently of the oceans, would have changed considerably over the last 50,000 years.

There is also the problem of contamination of atmospheric carbon dioxide by the burning of fossil fuels (e.g. oil, coal and natural gas) containing little or no active carbon and which dilute the active carbon dioxide in the atmosphere. During the nineteenth and twentieth centuries a considerable proportion of inactive carbon dioxide has been added to the carbon cycle.[16] This means that, in radiocarbon dating, the standard used—that is, the *present* radiocarbon content of carbon dioxide, upon which radiocarbon age calculations are based—is incorrect. This standard, however, could be modified so as to make it correct for the time immediately before the Industrial Revolution. It has been found, however, that the amount of active carbon in the atmosphere varied even before the Industrial Revolution.[17]

Moreover, to complicate matters even further, the amount of radiocarbon has been steadily increasing since the middle of the last century with the advent of atomic devices that have released neutrons into the atmosphere. These neutrons combine with atmospheric nitrogen to produce radiocarbon. The position is so bad that the scientists who work on radiocarbon dating disagree with one another as to the position and magnitude of these so-called 'short-term' fluctuations of the radiocarbon in our present atmosphere.[18] Each group of workers has its own particular standard upon which it bases the age of a particular sample, and this means that each group will give a different age for the same sample!

Scientists regard the fourth assumption—that dead organic matter is not later altered with respect to its carbon content by any biological or other activity—as being very important. The danger of contamination of the sample by external sources of carbon, especially in damp locations, has been recognized.[19] At a conference on radiocarbon dating held in 1956, the following remarks were made concerning this sort of contamination:

The most significant problem is that of biological alteration of materials in the soil. This effect grows more serious with greater age. To produce an error of 50 per cent. in the age of a 10,000 year old specimen would require the replacement of more than 25 per cent. of the carbon atoms. For a 40,000 year old sample, the figure is only 5 per cent. while an error of 5,000 years can be produced by about 1 per cent. of modern materials.[20]

One scientist working in the radiocarbon dating field has said that, because of contamination, 'we do not know which dates are in error, or by what amounts or why'.[21]

As we saw when looking at radiometric dating, the fifth assumption about a constant decay rate is the backbone of all radiometric dating. It has been generally assumed by scientists that the decay rates of radio-isotopes are independent of the physical and chemical environment. This is despite the fact that experimental evidence shows that this is not so.[22] What is even more surprising is that one of these experiments involves carbon, and this has far-reaching consequences for the radiocarbon method of dating.

Finally, for radiocarbon dating to be accurate, the sixth assumption has to be correct: that the rate of formation of radiocarbon in the upper atmosphere and its rate of disappearance from the biosphere are in equilibrium at present and have been so during the last 50,000 years. However, Professor Libby noted that there did not appear to be an equilibrium in the rate of formation and the rate of disappearance of radiocarbon at the present time—and if these rates are not in equilibrium at present, there is a very real doubt about whether they were in equilibrium in the past. This was a cause of concern for Professor Libby, since his calculations showed that, if the earth started with no radiocarbon in its atmosphere, it would take only up to 30,000 years to build up to the equilibrium position.[23] Although Professor Libby was aware of this non-equilibrium, he chose to ignore it, believing that the discrepancy was due to experimental error. But this discrepancy is very real: 'The Specific Production Rate (SPR) of C-14 is known to be 18.8 atoms per gram of total carbon per minute. The Specific Decay Rate (SDR) is known to be only 16.1 disintegrations per gram per minute.'[24] This represents a 14.4 per cent difference; how can an equilibrium condition be assumed with such a large difference existing? The truth of the matter is that this 14.4 per cent difference between the rate of formation and the rate of disappearance of radiocarbon makes all radiocarbon dating inaccurate.

In spite of these highly questionable assumptions, it is usually maintained that radiocarbon dating has been verified beyond any shadow of doubt by numerous correlations with samples of known age determined by other archaeological dating methods. *But this is not so!* Professor Libby pointed this out in his Nobel Prize acceptance lecture:

The first shock Dr Arnold and I had was when our advisers informed us that history extended back only to 5,000 years. We had thought initially that we would be able to get samples all along the curve back to 30,000 years, put the points in, and then our work would be finished. You read statements in books that such and such a society or archaeological site is 20,000 years old. We learned rather abruptly that these ancient ages are not known accurately; in fact, it is at about the time of the First Dynasty in Egypt that the first historical date of any real certainty has been established.[25]

It is pretty obvious, therefore, that any *genuine* correlation between definitely verified historical dates and the age found by the radiocarbon dating method is limited only to the last 5,000 years or so. Interestingly, the earlier part of this period of history is covered by biblical history.

From the arguments so far, it can be seen that radiocarbon dating applied to the last 50,000 years (even if such a time period existed) is highly suspect because of the invalid and often questionable assumptions which have to be made. There is, however, fairly good agreement among radiocarbon dates for the last 5,000 years or so of historically verified chronology, although there are numerous discrepancies and there is a very large margin of error the further back in time that comparisons are made. Moreover, the assumptions inherent in this method of dating are unlikely to be valid for periods distant in the past because of the universal cataclysmic Flood described in the book of Genesis, and because of the different terrestrial and atmospheric conditions which prevailed before the Flood and which are described in the first few chapters of the Bible.

However, there are results obtained by radiocarbon dating that completely undermine this method of dating and, by association, all other radiometric dating. Because of the relatively short half-life of radiocarbon, it can be shown that biological matter more than 100,000 years old would not contain any radiocarbon at all because it would all have decayed into nitrogen. However, radiocarbon has been found in wood samples trapped in lava flows the ages of which have been determined as millions of years old by other radiometric dating methods.[26] If the rocks are in fact millions of years old, any wood found in them would also be millions of years old and so should not contain any radiocarbon. This is not the only example. Radiocarbon has also been found in coal and diamonds found sandwiched between rock layers allegedly millions of years old. Radiocarbon dating performed on the coal and the diamonds give a radiocarbon age of only tens of thousands of years.[27] Such examples, as well as others discussed above, show not only the untrustworthiness of radiocarbon dating, but also the complete unreliability of radiometric dating in general.

Tree-ring dating

Although the radiocarbon dating method can be shown to be flawed, it is often argued that this method of dating has been verified by the independent method called 'dendrochronology', or tree-ring dating. This is not strictly correct, as we shall see. Dendrochronology is, on the face of it, simplicity itself—you count the number of tree rings and that gives the age of the tree. But it is not quite as simple as that, as can be seen from the following observations:

Firstly, tree rings are not two-dimensional structures. They are sheaths or layers of wood more or less completely surrounding the trunk, the branches, and the roots, formed in succession outward from pith to bark. 'Growth layer' is really a better term than tree ring, although the latter is in ordinary use.

Secondly, light and dark wood are commonly called spring and summerwood. These are terms referring to time, and until investigation proves them to be correct, descriptive terms such as lightwood and densewood are more precise.

Thirdly, the densewoods do not always end in sharp boundaries. Gradations may vary from sharp to diffuse. The lightwood of any single growth layer may even grade outward into densewood, which in turn may grade outward into lightwood. One question arises immediately: if a growth layer ends abruptly at one point in the stem of a tree, must it end similarly everywhere within the stem?

Fourthly, densewoods vary widely in thickness. Some densewoods may be 10–15 cells in thickness; others may have only one cell.

Fifthly, since lightwood is also variable, growth layers may be anywhere from 0.01 mm to 10 mm or more in thickness. A tree in a particular location may have growth layers that are uniform in thickness, whereas a tree in a different location has highly variable growth layers.

Sixthly, the term 'annual ring' implies a precise knowledge of the time of ring formation. It is, however, possible that factors that promote growth may fluctuate within the year as well as annually, depending on the local environment.[28]

In spite of all these problems, however, American dendrochronologists maintain that they have built up a substantial tree-ring chronology from the dendrochronological studies of the Bristlecone Pine tree (*Pinus aristata*), which is a very long-living tree (some attain ages of a few thousand years[29]) that grows high up in the White Mountains of California.[30] The tree-ring growth sequences are extracted in a borer and are the primary source for chronological data. However, the chronology is built up not merely by the microscopic counting of rings, but a large number of cores are examined, counted and compared in order to obtain a complete record of annual growth patterns over a few thousand years.

Now, simple ring-counting in a single-core specimen of Bristlecone Pine gives erroneous ages because of 'missing' rings.[31] Apparently, 5 per cent or more of the annual rings may be 'missing' along a given radius or core that spans many centuries. At least half of the 'missing' rings are usually found in their anticipated position through careful search of as little as 10 cm of circuit. The other 'missing' rings in a sample core are found by cross-checking its ring pattern with the ring patterns of other cores from trees in the same locality in which the 'missing' rings are present, or by checking against the ring record of the occasional specimen that contains every ring in a span of over 2,000 years. Dendrochronologists maintain that by such cross-checkings, a reliable chronology can be established—a master chronology of Bristlecone Pine tree rings. This chronology can then be used as an independent check on radiocarbon dating.

The problem is that this master chronology is, on the whole, unsuitable for samples to be checked against because the rings show little variation from year to year. This means that there are not enough 'markers' for cross-checking purposes. The dendrochronologist therefore resorts to radiocarbon dating in order to determine the 'age' of the Bristlecone Pine wood sample before an attempt is made to match it with the master chronology. Hence the Bristlecone Pine tree-ring dating is partially dependent upon radiocarbon dating, the inaccuracies of which have been described above. It is surprising, therefore, that dendrochronologists use this Bristlecone Pine master chronology to check the dates obtained by the radiocarbon dating method, given that radiocarbon dating is used to give an idea of the age of a sample in the first place. This is the same circular reasoning that is used with regard to the age determination of rocks using index fossils, described earlier in this chapter.

Scientific evidence for a young earth

Having established the total unreliability of current dating methods, we must now look at some of the scientific evidence that points to the fact that we are, in fact, living on a *young* earth. This evidence comes from a variety of scientific disciplines—astronomy, physics, geology and biology—and all of it leads us to the inevitable conclusion that the age of the earth should be measured in thousands of years rather than thousands of millions of years. Although this evidence exists and is readily available—for example, on the websites of creation organizations and in articles and books written by creationists—it is unfortunately not given the publicity in the mainstream media that it deserves.

The first piece of evidence for us to consider is the number of supernova remnants that we observe in our galaxy. A supernova occurs when a star explodes; on average, this happens about once every twenty-five years in our galaxy. Supernovae are extremely luminous and are often visible from the earth even during daylight hours for several days or weeks before they gradually fade from view. The gas and dust remnants from such explosions (like the famous Crab Nebula that we will look at in Chapter 6) expand outwards rapidly and should remain visible for over a million years. Yet the nearby parts of our galaxy in which we could observe such gas and dust shells contain only about 200 supernova remnants—a number which is consistent with only about 7,000 years of time.[32]

Another piece of evidence that points to a young earth is the lifetime of comets, especially those that orbit the sun in less than 150 years. The head of a comet is like a huge dirty snowball some 100 km in diameter. As it approaches the sun, a comet gains a tail as particles of dust and ice are blown off the comet's head by high-energy emissions from the sun. As a result, each time a comet orbits close to the sun, it loses so much of its material that many of these comets could not survive for much longer than 10,000 years.[33] As comets are supposed to be the same age as the solar system—that is, 4,600 million years—there is a problem for evolutionists, because the disintegration of comets proves that the solar system is only a few thousand years old. In order to explain this, evolutionists assume that comets come from an unobserved spherical 'Oort Cloud' which is located well beyond the orbit of Pluto. They then argue that improbable gravitational interactions with infrequently passing stars knock comets into the solar system, and that other improbable interactions with the large outer planets of the solar system slow them down. The result of such improbable events is the hundreds of comets currently observed in the solar system. The problem with this is that there is absolutely *no evidence* that the Oort Cloud exists: 'Many scientific papers are written each year about the Oort Cloud, its properties, its origin, its evolution. Yet there is not a shred of direct observational evidence for its existence.'[34]

The simple fact is that the lifetimes of comets show that the solar system (and hence the earth) is merely a few thousand years old. As such a conclusion is so unacceptable to evolutionary astronomers, they have invented a cloud of comets that no one has ever observed and for existence of which there is no evidence.

The next piece of scientific evidence that points to the fact that we are living on a young earth comes from the simple fact that the earth's magnetic field is decaying too fast. This argument was developed by the late Dr Thomas G. Barnes, who, until his death in October 2001, was emeritus Professor of Physics at the University of Texas at El Paso. In recent years, the argument has been refined by the well-known creationist Dr Russell Humphreys. In very simple terms, it has been shown that electrical resistance in the earth's core causes the electrical current that produces the earth's magnetic field to lose energy rapidly. As a result, the total energy stored in the earth's magnetic field is decreasing with a half-life of 1,465 ($\pm$ 165) years.[35] It has been shown that, given that rate, the magnetic field (and hence the earth), cannot be more than 20,000 years old.[36]

The fourth piece of evidence that we are living on a young earth actually comes from the fossil record. Soft-tissue cell-like microstructures, flexible and fibrous bone material, transparent and pliable blood vessels and red blood cells have been discovered in a *Tyrannosaurus rex* bone that is supposed to be over sixty-five million years old.[37] These discoveries made by Dr Mary Schweitzer, and other material found by her and her colleagues since the early 1990s, will be dealt with again in Chapter 8 (under 'Dinosaurs, birds and evolution'). Undecomposed DNA has also been discovered in a fossilized magnolia leaf that comes from the Clarikia Fossil Beds in North India.[38] The leaf is supposed to be seventeen million years old. These discoveries are a real problem for evolutionists because such material is not supposed to exist for longer than a few thousand years. Hence these findings alone show that the sedimentary rocks and the fossils that they contain cannot be millions of years old. This, in turn, means that the earth cannot be millions of years old and that its age should therefore be measured in thousands of years instead.

More evidence for a young earth comes from the rapid formation of geological features such as rock strata, canyons, drumlins and land formations such as hills, cliffs, beaches and lagoons. Such geological phenomena are well documented[39] and further testify to the fact that the age of the earth should be measured in thousands rather than thousands of millions of years.

As we have already noted, radiometric dating is often cited as proof that the earth is billions of years old. It may come as a surprise, therefore, to realize that this method of dating can also be used to show that the age of the earth should be measured in thousands rather than thousands of millions of years. First of all, we will look at the decay of uranium and thorium. As the radio-isotopes of these two elements decay, they emit *alpha* particles, which are helium-4 nuclei. As these *alpha* particles slow down, they pick up electrons to form helium-4 atoms. Now, this helium-4 migrates quickly through the earth's crust into the atmosphere. It is possible to calculate the amount of helium-4 being produced by the decay of uranium and thorium, because we know the amount of these two elements in the earth's crust. It is also possible to determine the amount of helium-4 in the atmosphere. Hence the age of the atmosphere can be calculated simply by dividing the amount of helium-4 in the atmosphere by the rate at which it is being added to the atmosphere. This calculation gives the age of the atmosphere as just over 11,000 years—a time period that is considerably less than the thousands of millions of years quoted by evolutionists and one that is more consistent with the age that is determined from the Scriptures.

The other radiometric dating method that can be used to show that we are living on a young earth is radiocarbon dating. When we considered radiocarbon dating earlier, we saw that there is not an equilibrium between the rate of formation of radiocarbon in the upper atmosphere and its rate of disappearance from the biosphere. I have shown elsewhere[40] that, from this imbalance, we can calculate that the upper age for the earth's atmosphere is 10,500 years—a time that is again consistent with the biblical account of the earth's creation and early history. This figure is again far short of the thousands of millions of years demanded by evolutionists. Furthermore, we have seen that radiocarbon has been found in coal and diamonds found sandwiched between rock layers alleged to be millions of years old, and that radiocarbon dating performed on the coal and the diamonds gave a radiocarbon age measured in thousands of years.

In an editorial in the prestigious journal *Science* on 8 January 1982, it was stated that 'those who propound creationism … have no substantial body of experimental data to back their prejudices'. This simply is not so, as we have seen in this chapter—particularly in this final section. We have seen that, contrary to what many people think, there is scientific evidence to show that the age of the earth should be measured in terms of thousands rather than thousands of millions of years.

Conclusion

In this chapter, we have looked at the problems faced by evolutionists in dating rocks. Although they confidently inform us that such and such a rock is so many millions of years old, we have seen that such dates are meaningless. This is because the dates are determined by a process of circular reasoning: rocks are dated by their fossils, and the fossils are dated by their supposed evolution, which, in turn, is proved by the dates of the rocks in which the fossils are found. Looking at radiometric dating, we saw that this, too, gives to rocks dates that are meaningless. The reason for this is that the assumptions made inevitably make radiometric dating inaccurate, as we have observed. We have concluded that radiometric dating is totally unreliable when put to the test. We saw that rocks, known to be less than a couple of hundred years old, are dated to be thousands, sometimes millions and sometimes thousands of millions of years old. Different dating methods consistently give different (so-called 'discordant') dates. Put simply, radiometric dating, even radiocarbon dating, cannot be trusted.

Finally, however, we saw that there is scientific evidence from a variety of scientific disciplines—astronomy, geomagnetism, palaeontology, geomorphology and radiometric dating—to show that we are living on a young earth, just as taught in the Scriptures. We should not be afraid of those who tell us that we cannot trust the Bible because they *know* that the earth is billions of years old and this disproves the Bible. Such people are putting their trust in fallible dating methods rather than in the infallible Word of God.

Notes

1 Lyell stated that his intention was to 'free the science from Moses' in June 1830 in a letter to George Scrope. See the article at: amen.org.uk/studies/rh/new_panorama.htm.

2 **Charles Darwin,** On the Origin of Species (London: Penguin, 1968), p. 293.

3 Taken from **J. P. Riley** and **G. Skirrow,** (eds.), Chemical Oceanography, vol. i (London: Academic Press, 1965), p. 164.

4 **Henry Morris,** (ed.), Scientific Creationism (San Diego: Creation-Life, 1974).

5 **W. K. Hensley** and **W. A. Bassett,** 'Pressure Dependence of the Radioactive Decay Constant of Beryllium-7', in Science, 181/4104 (1973), pp. 1164–1165.

6 **J. L. Anderson,** Abstract of Papers for the 161st National Meeting, American Chemical Society, Los Angeles (1971).

7 **H. S. Slusher,** Critique of Radiometric Dating (San Diego: Institute for Creation Research, 1973), p. 18; **R. M. Allen,** 'The Evaluation of Radiometric Evidence on the Age of the Earth', in Journal of the American Scientific Affiliation (December 1952), p. 18; **R. V. Gentry,** 'Cosmological Implications of Extinct Radioactivity from Pleochroic Haloes', in Creation Research Society Quarterly, 3/20 (1966), pp. 17–20.

8 **R. Humphreys,** 'Young Helium Diffusion Age of Zircons Supports Accelerated Nuclear Decay', in **Larry Vardiman, Andrew A. Snelling** and **Eugene F. Chaffin,** (eds.), Radioisotopes and the Age of the Earth, vol. ii (Green Forest, AR: Master Books, 2005), p. 74.

9 See, for example, **J. P. Kirkaldy,** Geological Time (Edinburgh: Oliver & Boyd, 1971), pp. 70–71.

10 Taken from **Bodie Hodge,** 'How Old is the Earth?', in **Ken Ham,** (ed.), The New Answers Book 2 (Green Forest, AR: Master Books, 2008), p. 194.

11 **D. E. Fisher,** Nature Physical Science, vol. 232 (19 July 1971), pp. 60–61.

12 These tables are taken from **Mike Riddle,** 'Does Radiometric Dating Prove the Earth is Old?', in **Ham,** (ed.), The New Answers Book, pp. 121–122.

13 Nobel Lectures: Chemistry 1942–1962 (Amsterdam: Elsevier, 1964), pp. 587–612.

14 From **J. L. Kulp,** 'The Carbon-14 Method of Age Determination', in Scientific Monthly, vol. 75 (November 1952), p. 261; **Henry M. Morris** and **John C. Whitcomb,** The Genesis Flood (London: Evangelical Press, 1969), pp. 371–373.

15 A. E. Trueman, *An Introduction to Geology* (London: Thomas Murby, 1945), p. 208.

16 H. R. Brannon et al., 'Radiocarbon Evidence on the Dilution of Atmospheric and Oceanic Carbon', in *Transactions, American Geophysical Union*, vol. 38 (October 1957), p. 650.

17 H. de Vries and **H. T. Waterbolk,** 'Groningen Radio Carbon Dates III', in *Science*, vol. 128 (19 December 1958), p. 1551.

18 Ingrid U. Olson, (ed.), *Radiocarbon Variations and Absolute Chronology* (New York: Wiley Interscience, 1970).

19 C. B. Hunt, 'Radio Carbon Dating in the Light of Stratigraphy and Weathering Processes', in *Scientific Monthly*, vol. 81 (November 1955), p. 240.

20 F. Johnson, J. R. Arnold and **R. F. Flint,** 'Radio Carbon Dating', in *Science*, vol. 125 (8 February 1957).

21 Hunt, 'Radio Carbon Dating', p. 240.

22 Hensley and **Bassett,** 'Pressure Dependence of the Radioactive Decay Constant of Beryllium-7', pp. 1164–1165; **J. L. Anderson,** Abstract of Papers for the 161st National Meeting, American Chemical Society, Los Angeles (1971).

23 Willard Libby, *Radiocarbon Dating* (Chicago: University of Chicago Press, 1952), p. 8.

24 C. Sewell, 'Carbon-14 and the Age of the Earth', 8 November 1999, at: www.rae.org/bits23.htm.

25 *Nobel Lectures: Chemistry 1942–1962*, pp. 587–612.

26 Andrew Snelling, 'Conflicting "Ages" of Tertiary Basalt and Contained Wood, Crinum, Central Queensland, Australia', in *Technical Journal*, 14/2 (2005), pp. 99–122.

27 John Baumgardner, '¹⁴C Evidence for a Recent Global Flood and a Young Earth', in **Vardiman et al.,** (eds.), *Radioisotopes and the Age of the Earth: Results of a Young-Earth Creationist Research Initiative* (Santee, CA: Institute for Creation Research; Chino Valley, AZ: Creation Research Society, 2005), pp. 587–630.

28 W. S. Glock and **S. Agerter,** 'Anomalous Patterns in Tree Rings', in *Endeavour*, vol. 22 (1963), pp. 9–13.

29 E. Schulman, 'Bristlecone Pine, Oldest Known Living Thing', in *National Geographic Magazine*, 113/3 (1958), pp. 354–372.

30 C. W. Ferguson, 'Dendrochronology of Bristlecone Pine, *Pinus aristata*: Establishment of a 7484-Year Chronology in the White Mountains of Eastern-Central California, USA', in **Ingrid U. Olsson,** (ed.), *Radiocarbon Variations and Absolute Chronology* (Nobel Symposium No. 12; New York: Wiley Interscience, 1970).

31 C. W. Ferguson, 'Bristlecone Pine: Science and Esthetics', in *Science*, 159/3817 (1968), pp. 839–846.

32 K. Davies, 'Distribution of Supernova Remnants in the Galaxy', in *Proceedings of the Third International Conference on Creationism*, vol. ii (Pittsburgh: Creation Science Fellowship, 1994), pp. 175–184.

33 R. A. Littleton, *Mysteries of the Solar System* (Oxford: Clarendon Press, 1968), p. 110.

34 Carl Sagan and A. Druyan, *Comet* (London: Headline, 1997), p. 210.

35 D. R. Humphreys, 'The Earth's Magnetic Field is Still Losing Energy', in *Creation Research Society Quarterly*, 39/1 (2002), pp. 3–13.

36 Thomas G. Barnes, *Origin and Destiny of the Earth's Magnetic Field* (San Diego: Institute for Creation Research, 1983).

37 Mary Higby Schweitzer, Jennifer L. Wittmeyer and John R. Horner, 'Soft Tissue and Cellular Preservation in Vertebrate Skeletal Elements from the Cretaceous to the Present', in *Proceedings of the Royal Society*, B22, 274/1607 (2007), pp. 183–197.

38 Edward M. Golenberg et al., 'Chloroplast DNA Sequence from a Miocene Magnolia Species', in *Nature*, vol. 344 (12 April 1990), pp. 656–658.

39 See, for example, the author's talk entitled *Geological Time Bombs* (DVD; Biblical Foundations, Pontyclun, and Two By Two Ltd, Chesterfield, 2009).

40 A. J. Monty White, *How Old is the Earth?* (Welwyn: Evangelical Press, 1985), pp. 88–91.

Chapter 6

The origin of the universe

A stronomy is the science of the study of the stars. The word 'astronomy' literally means 'star arranging', as it is derived from two Greek words: *astro* meaning 'star' and *nomos* meaning 'arranging'. The Oxford English Dictionary defines astronomy as 'the science of the heavenly bodies'. It has come to mean the study of the general history and development of the universe, including cosmology, the study of its origin.

Astronomy is a very popular science—it is often called everyone's 'second science'. It is probably the relationship between philosophy and astronomy that gives the latter such universal appeal. When we gaze into the heavens and consider the stars, we cannot help but ask questions like: Where do stars come from? When did the universe begin? Who or what is responsible for its existence? These are not trivial questions. They are questions upon which scientists, philosophers and the 'man in the street' have pondered for centuries. This was amply exemplified by atheist Isaac Asimov, when he wrote, 'Perhaps in an infinite sea of nothingness, globs of positive and negative energy in equal-sized pairs are constantly forming, and after passing through evolutionary changes, combining once more and vanishing. We are in one of those globs in the period of time between nothing and nothing, and wondering about it.'[1]

Although it had its roots in Egypt, Babylon, Greece and China, it was not until Galileo used his telescope for astronomical observations in 1609 that astronomy began to develop as a science. This development was aided by the application of scientific method and principles developed by such people as Copernicus, Galileo, Brahe, Kepler and Newton. We are now in the period that has been called 'post-modern astronomy, witnessing the progress of a revolution begun theoretically by Einstein and Friedmann and observationally by Hubble'.[2] Yet the post-modern astronomer still asks the age-old questions: What kind of universe do we live in? What is its shape and size? Where did it come from?

The nature of the universe
In 1927 the famous British geneticist J. B. S. Haldane remarked that it was

his suspicion that the universe was, in his own words, 'not only queerer than we suppose, but it is queerer than we *can* suppose'.[3] Haldane meant 'stranger' when he used the word 'queerer'. In this section, I propose to undertake a quick tour of the universe in order to give us an idea of its nature and to see if Haldane was right to conclude that the universe is stranger than we can imagine. In order to do this, we will need to use the unit of distance that astronomers use—the light year. This is the *distance* that light travels in a year. Light travels about 186,000 miles in a *second*. This means that, if we could travel at the speed of light, we would be able to go around the earth about 7.5 times in a second! A light year is truly an enormous distance—it is about six trillion miles.[4] One of the problems using a light year as a unit to measure distance is the confusion sometimes caused by the word 'year'; some people think that time rather than distance is being referred to. This really should not be a problem so long as you keep firmly in your mind the fact that a light year is a measure of distance, not time.

The planet earth is, on average, 7,926 miles in diameter at its equator; it revolves on its axis once every day, and travels at a speed which varies between 65,520 and 67,750 miles per hour around the sun. It takes a year for the earth to go once around the sun, which is on average about 92.6 million miles away—about 91 million miles away when the earth is at *perihelion* (that is, when it is nearest to the sun) and about 94.5 million miles away when the earth is at *aphelion* (that is, when it is furthest from the sun). This distance to the sun is too big for many to grasp, so it tends to become meaningless. In order to put it into some type of perspective, imagine that you are travelling in a car at seventy miles per hour. At this speed, it would take you over 151 years to get to the sun. Our sun is a yellow dwarf star, which has a mean diameter of 864,327 miles. The sun can be thought of as a huge thermonuclear reactor in which 570 million tons of hydrogen are converted into 566 million tons of helium *every second*. This means that the sun is losing 4 million tons of its mass every second. But there is no need to worry. Even at this rate of 'burning', the sun will not 'burn out' for thousands of millions of years!

The sun and the stars that can be seen from the earth are in a galaxy which we call the Milky Way. This galaxy, which is shaped like two huge fried eggs placed back to back, contains over 100 billion stars. The whole galaxy is rotating at such a rate that the sun, which is about two-thirds of the distance from the centre of the Milky Way, would take about 225 to 250 million years to complete one revolution (called the galactic year). Our galaxy is about 100,000 light years across (that's about 600 quadrillion miles), and about 1,000 light years deep (that's about six quadrillion miles) at the centre. The size of our Milky Way galaxy, compared with that of our solar system, is almost unimaginable. If the diameter of our solar system were represented by one inch, then, on this scale, the diameter of the Milky Way would be about 1,300 miles. The Milky Way is known to have about eighteen satellite galaxies—these are much smaller galaxies than the Milky Way and orbit it because of gravitational attraction. With these distances in mind, our nearest star-neighbour, *Proxima Centauri*, is practically on our doorstep, being 4.24 light years away—a mere twenty-five trillion miles; it would take over forty million years to travel this distance in a car travelling at seventy miles per hour.

Much further away is our nearest galaxy-neighbour, the Andromeda Galaxy, with its nineteen satellite galaxies. It is called the Andromeda Galaxy because it is found in the constellation of Andromeda. It is about 2.5 million light years away—that's about fifteen quintillion miles. It is estimated that there are something like 100 billion galaxies in the universe. This means that there are about as many galaxies in the universe as there are stars in a galaxy! The universe therefore contains somewhere in the order of ten sextillion stars. To grasp this number, consider that, if you could count up to three million *every second*, then it would take over *a hundred million years* to count ten sextillion. Finally, the universe itself is thought to be something like 13,700 million light years in radius, which means that it is 27,400 million light years in diameter. This distance is a staggering 165 sextillion miles. Travelling at the speed of light, it would take about 27,400 million years to get from one side of the universe to the other. These staggering distances should give us an idea of the size of the universe and also make us realize the greatness of the God who created it.

We will now consider some of the enormous variety of stars that we find in this huge universe, for this, too, is truly amazing. Stars have colours ranging from red to orange, yellow, white, and even bluish-white. Not only do they have differing colours, but the brightness of the stars also ranges from 100,000 times the brightness of the sun down to one ten-thousandth of the brightness of the sun. Some stars even have variable brightness. Two stars sometimes revolve around each other—these are called binary stars. Star clusters are also common. The size of stars also varies. Some stars, called dwarfs, are of comparable size to that of the earth but are much heavier. An egg-cup full of the matter of a white dwarf star, for example, would weigh several thousand tons! At the other end of the scale there are the giants. If the sun was placed in the centre of the red giant star Betelgeuse[5] so that their centres coincided, the earth would also be inside the star, millions of miles away from its surface!

An even more fascinating type of star is the neutron star. These are about five to ten miles in radius and are composed completely of neutrons. The neutrons are so closely packed together that the stars have a density of about 100 trillion times that of water. This means that a gallon bucket full of neutron star dust would weigh something like 500 billion tons and would take about 5,000 years to empty if the star dust was poured out at a rate of three tons per second!

The famous Crab Nebula has such a neutron star at its centre. This nebula is the result of a star that was seen to explode in broad daylight by Chinese astronomers on 4 July 1054. The Crab Nebula is about 6,500 light years away and about 60 trillion miles across, and it is expanding at a rate of about 1,000 miles per second. The neutron star at the centre of the Crab Nebula is spinning very rapidly (30.2 times per second!) and it has on its surface a particular area which emits radio frequencies. As the star rotates, this radiation sweeps through space in a narrow beam similar to light from a lighthouse. Hence astronomers observe 30.2 pulses of radiation per second on their radio-telescopes—such a pulsating radio star is called a 'pulsar'. Hundreds of pulsars have been discovered since the first pulsar (designated 'CP 1919') was identified in July 1967. However, when the radiation of CP 1919 was first detected in the middle of the twentieth century, it was not known what it was. Because of the seemingly unnatural regularity of its emissions—it had a regular period of 1.3373 seconds—the evolutionary astronomers designated it 'LGM-1', which stood for 'Little

Green Man One'—claiming it to be intelligent beings of extra-terrestrial origin who were trying to communicate with people on earth!

Finally, probably the most incredible stars in existence are called 'black holes'. Such stars are just a couple of miles or so in diameter and are again composed of neutrons packed so densely that 500 trillion tons of matter is packed into a sphere about the size of a football! The force of gravity at the surface of such a star is so great that it prevents any light from leaving the surface—hence the star appears black even though it may be white-hot. Although black holes cannot be seen directly, their presence can be inferred from the gravitational influence they exert on nearby stars. In January 2005, astronomers from the University of California, Los Angeles, presented evidence that, some 30,000 light years away, tens of thousands of black holes are orbiting a monstrous black hole at the centre of the Milky Way.[6]

The Big Bang

Among evolutionists, the Big Bang is the most popular and probably the most widely held view of the origin of the universe. It must be pointed out that not all cosmologists accept the Big Bang theory, and views about the origin of the universe are constantly changing. Basically, the Big Bang hypothesis states that the universe began with an infinitesimally small, and infinitely hot and dense, point that is called a 'singularity'. This singularity is supposed to have contained not only all the mass and energy of the universe, but also 'space' itself. According to this hypothesis, at time equals zero, about 13.7 billion years ago, the singularity expanded rapidly, giving rise to the universe that we observe today.

One of the questions that immediately springs to mind is: Where did this singularity come from? To try to answer this question, cosmologists run into problems with explanations that simply do not make sense. If 'when the singularity started to expand' is the moment at which time started, then the question that we have just asked is meaningless. It is illogical to ask what existed *before* time began. However, cosmologists suggest that before the Big Bang there was nothing—no space, no time, no matter, no energy—absolutely nothing. This could be thought of as 'absolute nothingness'. It is interesting to note that the popular astronomer Heather

Couper and her co-author Nigel Henbest have, in their book *Big Bang*, stated that the nothing before the Big Bang 'was a "nothing" so profound it defies human comprehension'.[7] Indeed it does! When we think of 'nothing', we tend to think of dark, empty space. But this is not 'nothing'— it is dark, empty space. So if we have 'nothing' and leave it for hundreds of millions of years, nothing will happen—it certainly won't explode! But there is a problem there, too: there is no time if you have 'nothing', so it cannot exist for hundreds of millions of years. One can therefore argue that the Big Bang hypothesis states that 'In the beginning nothing exploded'. It is interesting to contrast this with what the Bible teaches in Genesis 1:1: that 'In the beginning God created ...'

It is not just creationists who are wary of believing that the universe came from nothing without the intervention of any supernatural agent. British astronomer and science writer David Darling has also sounded the following note of caution:

Don't let the cosmologists try to kid you on this one. They have not got a clue either ... 'In the beginning,' they will say, there was nothing—no time, space, matter, or energy. Then there was a quantum fluctuation from which—whoa! Stop right there. You see what they mean? First there is nothing and then there is something—and before you know it, they have pulled a hundred billion galaxies out of their quantum hats.[8]

In fact, it is difficult to imagine how *anything* can exist if *nothing* exists! However, to get around this, the cosmologists maintain that the laws of physics are in operation even when there is nothing. Cosmologist Victor Stenger, emeritus Professor of Physics, University of Hawaii, has stated that 'the laws of physics are the laws of nothing' and that 'something is more stable than nothing'.[9] Victor Stenger is therefore maintaining that the same laws of physics existed when there was nothing as they do today when there is something. He believes that the laws of physics caused the universe to come into being because these laws determine that the universe is more stable than absolute nothingness. It has to be said that Professor Stenger (and those who embrace his arguments) is putting his faith in the laws of physics rather than in the Creator. Following Stenger's line of argument, Marcus Chown, who at the time of writing is cosmology consultant for *New Scientist*, has concluded, 'There is no need to imagine there being no laws of physics and then the laws of physics coming into being—along with everything else—in the Big Bang.'[10]

Basically, the cosmologists are fudging the issue. There is nothing—absolute nothingness—and yet, at the same time, there is something—the laws of physics. This really is a fudge; the cosmologists are asking us to believe that there never was a time when there was absolutely nothing, and that the laws of science—in this case, the laws of physics—have always existed, even before time existed! They are therefore asking us to believe that these laws have always existed and are responsible for the creation and subsequent development of the universe. Thus they replace God, the Creator and Sustainer of the universe, with the laws of physics.

A totally different explanation of how the universe came from nothing is that suggested by Neil Turok of the University of Cambridge and his colleague Paul Steinhardt of the University of Princeton, New Jersey. It has to be admitted that their explanation sounds more like science fiction than science. In fact, the details in this account are reminiscent of the story in *Alice in Wonderland*, when the Queen told Alice that when she was younger she believed as many as six impossible things before breakfast! We are used to thinking in four dimensions: length, breadth, height and time. Hence imagining more than four dimensions is extremely difficult, if not impossible. Similarly, imagining four dimensions when one of these is not time is equally difficult. In spite of this, these two scientists argue that, before the Big Bang, there were 'branes'—four-dimensional 'island universes'—and that these existed in a ten-dimensional space–time. They then argue that the Big Bang that caused our universe to come into existence was the result of the collision of two of these branes.[11] Such an explanation is so esoteric that it is difficult to bring any scientific arguments to bear on it.

If we assume that the Big Bang occurred, what is the account of the subsequent development of the universe? It has to be acknowledged that cosmologists' description of the Big Bang is subject to much speculation—primarily because no one was there to see it happen, if it happened at all. In the account I have set out below, the term 'explosion' is used; however, the Big Bang should not really be thought of as an explosion in the conventional sense. The universe—its space and time—is thought to be the result of its appearing (rather than 'exploding') from nothing. I have used the term 'explosion' to follow conventional descriptions of the Big Bang. Although the universe is thought to be expanding as a result of the Big Bang, it does not have a global centre and it is not expanding *into* anything; neither has it expanded *from* anything, because the universe is not embedded in *another* space—our universe *is* space. One of the best explanations of how to view this is provided by Peter Coles, Professor of Theoretical Astrophysics at Cardiff University:

This difficulty is often also confused in one's mind with the question of where the Big Bang actually happened: are we not moving away from the site of the original explosion? Where was this explosion situated? The answer to this is the explosion happened everywhere and everything is moving away from it. But in the beginning, at the Big Bang singularity, everywhere and everything was in the same place.[12]

So what is the cosmologists' account of the development of the universe? They point out that quantum theory[13] suggests that at 10^{-43} second after the beginning of the Big Bang—an infinitesimally short period of time after the initial explosion occurred—the four forces of nature—the strong nuclear, the weak nuclear, the electromagnetic and gravity—were combined as a single 'super force'. It is believed that quarks—the elementary particles which are the fundamental constituents of matter—began to bond together in trios, forming photons, positrons and neutrinos, and that these formed together with their anti-particles (particles that are identical except that they have opposite charges). Evolutionary cosmologists believe that minute amounts of protons and neutrons also formed at this stage—approximately one for every one billion photons, neutrinos or electrons. These cosmologists then tell us that at approximately 10^{-37} second after the Big Bang started, a phase transition caused what is called a 'cosmic inflation' to happen. This inflation period can be thought of as a time when the universe underwent a rate of expansion many times the speed of light. The size of the universe grew exponentially during this inflationary stage; it is believed that, in less than one thousandth of a second, the universe doubled in size at least 100 times.

This 'isotropic inflation' of the universe ended at 10^{-35} second after the beginning of the Big Bang, with the universe almost perfectly smooth. Cosmologists argue that, if it were not for a slight fluctuation in the density distribution of matter, galaxies would not have been able to form.

If all this sounds like science fiction, there is more, as the following story told by evolutionary cosmologists amply demonstrates. It is argued that, at the close of the inflationary period, the temperature of the universe was so high that the random motions of particles were at relativistic speeds (that is, speeds approaching the speed of light) and that particle–antiparticle pairs of all kinds were being continuously formed and destroyed in collisions. The cosmologists then believe that, at some point, an unknown reaction resulted in a very small excess of quarks and leptons (leptons are another family of elementary particles) over anti-quarks and anti-leptons—of the order of one part in thirty million. They believe that this resulted in the predominance of matter over anti-matter in the universe.

We are told that, after the inflation stopped, the universe was, at this point, composed of ionized plasma in which matter and radiation were inseparable. Additionally, cosmologists tell us that there were equal quantities of particles and anti-particles. However, when the universe was one hundredth of a second old, neutrons begin to decay on a massive scale, allowing free electrons and protons to combine with other elementary particles. It is believed that the formation of matter from energy was made possible by photons materializing into baryons and anti-baryons (baryons are made of three quarks), with their subsequent annihilations transforming them into pure energy. Cosmologists further believe that, because of these collisions and annihilations, matter was unable to remain viable for more than a few nanoseconds (10^{-9} second) before a bombardment of electrons would have scattered these photons.

Evolutionary cosmologists maintain that the universe continued to grow in size and the temperature continued to fall. They believe that, one full second after the initial explosion, the temperature of our universe had dropped to ten billion degrees Celsius. At this temperature, photons no longer have the energy to disrupt the formation of matter as well as transform energy into matter. After three minutes, it is believed that the temperature had dropped to one billion degrees Celsius, and the protons and neutrons were slowing down enough in order to allow nucleosynthesis—the formation of the nuclei of atoms—to take place. The cosmologists inform us that, at this stage, atomic nuclei of helium were produced as two protons and two neutrons bonded together. For every helium nucleus that was formed, there were apparently about ten protons left over, allowing for 25 per cent of the universe to be comprised of helium. We are told that the next important phase of the evolution of the universe occurred around thirty minutes later, when the formation of photons increased through the annihilation of electron–positron pairs. It is argued that the universe began with slightly more electrons than positrons, and that this ensured that our universe was able to form the way it did. According to the cosmologists, the next significant stage in the history of the universe happened about 379,000 years after the start of the Big Bang, when electrons and atomic nuclei combined into atoms (mostly hydrogen) and the radiation decoupled from matter and continued through space largely unimpeded. This relic radiation is known as the 'cosmic microwave background radiation'.

Then, the cosmologists inform us, over a long period of time, the slightly denser regions of the nearly uniformly distributed matter gravitationally attracted nearby matter. This means that these denser regions grew even denser, forming gas clouds, stars, galaxies and the other astronomical structures that we observe in the universe today.

Cosmologists believe that the universe today is dominated by a mysterious form of energy known as 'dark energy', which apparently permeates all of space. They believe that 72 per cent of the total energy density of today's universe is in this form. They maintain that, when it was very young, the universe was probably infused with dark energy. However, with less space, and with everything closer together, gravity had the upper hand, with the result that gravity slowed down the expansion. Eventually, after many billions of years of expansion, the growing abundance of dark energy caused the expansion of the universe to slowly begin to accelerate, and this is where we are today.

Problems with the Big Bang

Because of the popularity of the Big Bang theory, many people do not realize that not all scientists accept this explanation of the origin of the universe. In May 2004, a group of thirty-four secular scientists challenged the Big Bang theory in an open letter published in *New Scientist* and on the Internet.[14] By late spring 2009, 218 scientists and engineers, 187 independent researchers and 105 other people had added their signatures to this letter. In this letter, the thirty-four scientists addressed a number of problems associated with the Big Bang hypothesis. The letter begins,

The big bang today relies on a growing number of hypothetical entities, things that we have never observed—inflation, dark matter and dark energy are the most prominent examples. Without them, there would be a fatal contradiction between the observations made by astronomers and the predictions of the big bang theory. In no other field of physics would this continual recourse to new hypothetical objects be accepted as a way of bridging the gap between theory and observation. It would, at the least, raise serious questions about the validity of the underlying theory.

The letter then goes on to address other problems with the Big Bang theory, some of which I allude to below.

Cosmologists maintain that the Big Bang hypothesis makes two major predictions and that these have been observed and, as a consequence, have proved the Big Bang to be true. Let us look at both of these in order to determine whether these observations really do prove that the Big Bang happened or can be interpreted in other ways.

The first prediction concerns what is called the 'red shift'. If the universe is expanding, as predicted by the Big Bang, the galaxies should be moving away from one another at velocities proportional to the distances separating them. In 1924 the American astronomer Edwin Hubble invented a method for measuring the distances of galaxies. He also observed that, when the light coming from these distant galaxies was studied using an instrument called a spectrometer, the emission or absorption lines of the elements were not seen at their usual wavelengths, but were shifted towards the red end of the spectrum. Hubble and many other astronomers claimed that this 'red shift' is directly proportional to the velocity with which the galaxies are receding. It is found that, the more distant the galaxy, the greater is the observed 'red shift'—that is, the greater is its velocity—exactly what would be expected if the Big Bang were true. On the face of it, this seems to prove the Big Bang theory. But this observation that the universe is expanding is something that is taught in the Scriptures. The Bible teaches in a number of places that the universe has been 'stretched out' or expanded. For example, in Isaiah 40:22 we read that God stretches out the heavens like a curtain and spreads them out like a tent in which to dwell. Such verses of Scripture actually hint that the universe has increased in size since its creation—God has stretched it out, causing it to expand. The red shift, therefore, has nothing at all to do with the Big Bang—it is confirmation of the stretching out of the universe by the hand of the Creator.

The second prediction of the Big Bang hypothesis concerns the existence of what is called the 'cosmic microwave background radiation'. We saw above that, according to cosmologists, when the universe was about 379,000 years old, electrons and atomic nuclei combined into atoms (mostly hydrogen), and the radiation decoupled from matter and continued through space largely unimpeded. This relic radiation is what is known as the cosmic microwave background radiation. In June 1965, using a very sensitive radio-telescope, two researchers from the Bell Telephone Laboratories discovered microwave radiation coming apparently uniformly from all directions in space.[15] This cosmic microwave background radiation corresponded to about 3.5 K (about −270°C). The two scientists involved, Arno Penzias and Robert Wilson, were awarded the Nobel Prize in Physics in 1978 for the discovery of cosmic microwave background radiation, which was deemed to be the 'echo' of the Big Bang.

But is the cosmic microwave background radiation connected with the hypothetical Big Bang? In 1926, the famous British astrophysicist Sir Arthur Eddington had already provided an accurate explanation for this temperature found in space.[16] He showed that this phenomenon was not due to some ancient explosion, but rather was simply the background radiation from all of the heat sources (mostly the stars) that occupy the universe. He calculated the minimum temperature to which any particular body in space would cool and showed that it would be 3.18 K (later refined to 2.8)—essentially the same as the observed 'background' radiation that is known to exist today. Despite the strong opinions of the cosmologists who believe in the Big Bang, the idea that the cosmic microwave background radiation proves the Big Bang is not as reliable as they would like us to believe. This is borne out by a comment from evolutionist Karen Fox, who in 2002 confessed, 'This radiation [cosmic microwave background radiation] in and of itself doesn't require the big bang theory *per se* to be correct.'[17]

There is therefore no scientific proof of the Big Bang hypothesis—the fact that the galaxies appear to be receding from one another has a biblical explanation, and astrophysicists such as the late Sir Arthur Eddington have provided other scientific explanations for the cosmic microwave background radiation.

Earlier we saw that over 500 scientists and engineers have drawn the scientific community's attention to the fact that the Big Bang hypothesis relies on a growing number of hypothetical entities that have never been observed. Inflation, dark matter and dark energy are among these entities. In addition, there are another four scientific problems with the Big Bang:[18]

1. *The missing monopoles.* Monopoles are hypothetical massive particles that are just like magnets but have only one pole. Cosmologists maintain that many monopoles would have been formed in the high temperatures of the Big Bang and, since they are stable, they should still be in existence today. Yet none have been found, despite intense searching. The only logical conclusion that can be reached is that such high temperatures as those postulated in the Big Bang have never occurred, which in turn means that the Big Bang *never* occurred.

2. *The flatness problem.* The expansion rate of the universe appears to be very finely balanced with the force of gravity—this condition is known as 'flat'. If the universe were the result of the Big Bang, it is difficult to imagine how such an unlikely condition could have transpired.

3. *The missing anti-matter.* As we have seen, according to the Big Bang hypothesis, matter (in the form of hydrogen and helium) formed from energy as the universe expanded. However, whenever matter is formed from energy, anti-matter is also produced. Anti-matter has

similar properties to matter except that the charges of the particles that compose it are reversed. This means that equal quantities of matter and anti-matter should have been produced in the Big Bang and this should be observed today—but it is not! The visible universe is composed almost entirely of matter, which, in fact, is exactly what we would expect from what the Bible teaches. God created the universe composed of matter. If it were composed of equal amounts of matter and anti-matter, as required by the Big Bang, then, when the matter and anti-matter came together, they would violently destroy each other and life would not be possible. The fact that the universe contains life—at least in this corner of the universe—suggests that the Big Bang *never* occurred.

4. *The missing Population III stars.* The Big Bang hypothesis can only account for the existence of the three lightest elements: hydrogen, helium and lithium. The heavier elements are thought to form in the final stages of a star when it explodes (that is, in a supernova). So-called second- and third-generation stars are thus said to be 'contaminated' with small amounts of these heavier elements. Now, if the Big Bang had occurred, the first stars that formed in the universe would comprise only the three lightest elements. According to cosmologists, these so-called Population III stars should still be around, yet no such stars have ever been found! This is more evidence to suggest that the Big Bang *never* occurred.

Although cosmologists would have us believe that there is overwhelming evidence for believing that the Big Bang occurred, we have seen that, in reality, this is not so. Not only is there no explanation of how something (the universe) can come from nothing, but there is *no evidence* for the account of the history of the universe as told by the cosmologists who believe in the Big Bang. Without any evidence to substantiate their claims, they confidently tell us about inflation, which has never been seen, and about dark matter and dark energy, which have never been observed. The same cosmologists ridicule the idea of a Creator who stretched out the heavens, causing the universe to expand. They dismiss the explanation of the cosmic microwave background radiation that shows that it has nothing at all to do with the Big Bang but is a result of the minimum temperature to which any particular body in space would cool. Yet they can provide no explanation for the missing monopoles, the missing anti-matter, the missing Population III stars and the problem of the 'flatness' of the universe. The only conclusion that can be reached is that the Big Bang hypothesis does not stand up to scientific investigation and so should be dismissed as nothing more than the 'fairy story for grown-ups' that it is.

Before leaving this section, however, it is worth considering that there are in fact only four possibilities to explain the origin of the universe:
- It has always been here.
- It is not really here—it is an illusion.
- It came from nothing, naturally.
- It came from nothing, supernaturally.

Let us look at each of these possibilities in turn and see what conclusions we reach.

The *first* explanation is that the universe has always been here. If the universe had always existed, however, it would be infinitely old, and by now everything would have 'wound down' and nothing would be happening. In other words, by now there would be no energy left to do useful work as predicted by the second law of thermodynamics. Clearly, things are still happening in the universe—for example, I am alive and sitting in my house while writing this paragraph, and the sun is shining between the showers of rain. The fact that things are happening proves that the universe has not always been here—it must have had a beginning.

The *second* possibility is that the universe is not really here at all but is an illusion. This explanation is really ridiculous, because we have to exist in order to deny our existence!

The *third* possibility is the one that we have been considering in the last two sections of this chapter—that the universe arose naturally from nothing. We have seen that this, too, is a ridiculous explanation; we have seen that the account of the Big Bang is more like a fairy story for grown-ups than a sound scientific explanation of the origin and history of the universe.

We are therefore left with the *fourth* and only logical explanation for the origin of the universe—that it came supernaturally from nothing; 'In the beginning God created the heavens and the earth', as it says in the first verse of the first book of the Bible.

One or many universes?

We have seen, then, that the universe is incredibly vast and that it contains an unbelievable number and variety of stars. We have also seen that there is no adequate scientific explanation for the origin of the universe. Despite the fact that there is no scientific explanation or justification for the existence of our universe, some astronomers are not content to believe that there is only one universe, but now imagine that an infinite number of universes exist at the same time! This concept is called 'multiverses'.

The question that needs addressing is: Where do astronomers get the idea of multiverses from? Dr Craig Hogan, a cosmologist at the University of Washington, has answered this question by referring to the concept of the Big Bang origin of the universe—the belief, as we have seen, that the universe in which we live arose naturally out of nothing. Hogan has suggested that 'Once you've discovered it's easy to make a universe out of an ounce of vacuum, why not make a bunch of them?'[19]

The consequences of such an idea have been spelled out by Marcus Chown, the *New Scientist*'s cosmology consultant, as follows:

Far, far away in a galaxy with a remarkable resemblance to the Milky Way, sits a star that looks remarkably like the Sun. And on the star's third planet, which looks remarkably like the Earth, lives someone who, for all the world, looks like your identical twin. Not only do they look the same as you but they are reading this exact same book—in fact they are focused on this very line. Actually, it is weirder than this. A whole lot weirder. There is an infinite number of galaxies that look just like our own galaxy, containing an infinite number of versions of you whose lives, leading up until this moment, have been absolutely identical to yours.[20]

Marcus Chown informs us that this is not science fiction but an 'unavoidable consequence of the standard theory of our Universe'.[21] By this, he means that the idea of the existence of multiverses is the result of the Big Bang that apparently caused our universe to come into existence. This means that, if you accept the Big Bang, you have to accept the idea of there being an infinite number of people who are identical to you existing in an infinite number of universes. And they will be reading this same book *at the same time as you are reading it*, and this same book will have been written by an identical Dr Monty White in these parallel universes!

Is there any evidence that these parallel universes exist? An interesting consequence of believing in the idea of multiverses is that it is impossible to move from one universe to another universe, despite some ingenious science-fiction stories about transferring to a parallel universe.[22] As it is impossible to observe one of these universes from another universe, multiverses are therefore beyond the realm of scientific experimentation. This means that no scientific tests can be conducted to determine whether or not such multiverses exist; no falsifiable predictions can therefore be made—such predictions being the backbone of scientific endeavour. The idea of multiverses is, therefore, nothing more than wishful thinking, and is not supported by any scientific data.

It is my experience that many Christians, when confronted with this scenario of multiverses, are confused and simply do not know how to respond. They feel that their understanding of the origin and nature of the universe is so woefully inadequate that they are not able to argue against multiverses, and so perhaps think that clever scientists have proven the existence of their doppelgängers. However, we must be biblical in all our thinking, so we must argue biblically. The Scriptures tell us quite plainly in Romans 6:10 and in Hebrews 10:10 that the Lord Jesus Christ died *once*— here on planet earth—to save us from our sins. There were not an infinite number of Sons of God dying an infinite number of deaths for an infinite number of sinners on an infinite number of earths! Although this is a spiritual argument, it is another strong argument for the non-existence of multiverses.

The understandableness of the universe

Have you ever wondered why it is that you can understand the universe in which we live? Why is it that you, the reader, can grasp the description of the universe that I wrote above? What makes the universe understandable? These are not idle questions and they do have a rational (as well as a spiritual) answer. But before we look at the answer, let me tell you that if you have ever asked such questions, you are in good company; the famous physicist and Noel laureate Albert Einstein also pondered this when he proclaimed that 'The most incomprehensible thing about the universe is that it is comprehensible'.[23]

This means that, when we investigate the universe, no matter how mathematical, esoteric, complicated or counter-intuitive is the description or explanation of a particular observable fact, we are able to figure it out and make sense of it. We use intelligence, intuition and imagination in order to understand it—and that is what makes us human. That is what makes us different from animals; a pet dog or cat, for instance, has no interest in understanding the universe in which we live. Why is this? The reason is that members of the human race are not like the animals, but are made in the image and likeness of God; therefore it is reasonable and logical for us to be able to comprehend the universe which God has created.

It is interesting to note, however, that the God who created the universe is himself incomprehensible—he can never be fully understood. Yet, at the same time, he is knowable. In one sense, there is no answer to the question that Isaiah asked: 'To whom then will you liken God? Or what likeness will you compare to Him?' (Isa. 40:18). Yet the Lord Jesus Christ prayed in what is the real Lord's Prayer in John 17: 'And this is eternal life, that they may know You, the only true God, and Jesus Christ whom You have sent' (John 17:3).

Christians have always been aware of these two apparently contradictory notions: that God, who is incomprehensible, can be known. The early Christian Fathers, for example, spoke of the invisible God as an unbegotten, nameless, eternal, incomprehensible, unchangeable being, and yet, at the same time, confessed that God reveals himself in and through the Lord Jesus Christ, and therefore can be known unto salvation. God can be known, but it is impossible for men and women to have a knowledge of God that is exhaustive and perfect in every way. Yet it is possible for us to obtain a knowledge of God that is perfectly adequate for the realization of the divine purpose in our lives. True knowledge of God can be acquired only from the divine self-revelation (that is, God's communicating knowledge of himself to men and women) and only to those who accept this with childlike faith. Christianity necessarily presupposes such a knowledge.

We read in the Bible that God has revealed himself to us through various names, yet the Bible often speaks of the name of God in the singular (for example, in the third commandment found in Exod. 20:7). In such instances, 'the name' stands for the whole manifestation of God in his relation to his people. The simplest name used for God in the Old Testament is the Hebrew *El*, and this conveys the meaning of being first, being Lord, of being strong and mighty. The name *Adonai* points to God as the almighty Ruler, whereas *Shaddai* and *El Shaddai* are used to show that God possesses all power in heaven and on earth. Through the name *Yahweh*, God reveals himself as the God of grace. In the New Testament we find the Greek equivalents of the Old Testament Hebrew names. For *El* we find *Theos*, which is the most common name for God; *Yahweh* and *Adonai* are usually rendered *Kurios*, which is derived from the Greek word *kuros*, meaning 'power'. We also find that *Pater*, meaning father, is used repeatedly in the New Testament.

What else does the Bible teach about God? One thing we learn as we read the Scriptures is that God has certain qualities that theologians refer to as 'attributes'. Some of these are termed 'incommunicable attributes'; they include God's self-existence, his immutability, his infinity and his unity. These are part of what might be called the 'constitutional nature' of God. God's other attributes are termed 'communicable attributes' and emphasize his personal nature. These include his spirituality, his intellectual attributes (the knowledge, wisdom and veracity of God), his moral attributes (the goodness, holiness and righteousness of God), and his sovereignty.

What has this got to do with our understanding of the universe? Not so very long ago, those who studied the so-called natural sciences attempted to relate their discoveries to God's natural revelation. For example, the science and study of astronomy was seen to be the study of God's handiwork (Ps. 19:1); natural history was seen to be the study of God's creation and design; and the laws of science were seen to be God's laws. Indeed, scientists often dedicated their books and scientific theses to God, and some spoke of thinking God's thoughts after him. It used to be believed (and still is by Christians) that the laws of science hold true and are unchanging because of what the Bible teaches about God and about his involvement with his creation: 'The LORD our God, the LORD is one!' (Deut. 6:4); 'And He is before all things, and in Him all things consist' (Col. 1:17); 'Jesus Christ is the same yesterday, today, and forever' (Heb. 13:8).

Because of who God is—the only one, true God—and because he is involved with his creation not only in the present but also in the past and future, it follows that we should expect a unity in the natural order and in the universe—in the past, present and future. It follows that the scientists' belief in the unchanging laws of nature is not because a brief 500 years of scientific measurement have shown that there is stability, but because these laws reflect God, who is unvarying and unwavering. Scientists may not be aware of this and may even reject it—but nevertheless it is so. The universality of the laws of science determines that the laws of science that are in operation today were in operation yesterday and that they will be in operation tomorrow (that is the *time* element); and that these same laws are in operation throughout the entire universe (that is the *dimensional* element). If we remove belief in the one eternal God who is the Creator and Sustainer of the entire universe, we have the possibility of quite different laws operating at different times and in different places in the universe. But observations that we have made in the past, not only on earth but also in other parts of the universe, actually confirm the universality of the laws of science.

It is obvious from the Bible that to create everything, God used different laws from the natural laws with which he now sustains the universe. This actually means that all attempts to discover or date the origin of the universe, of life and of people are outside the scope of scientific method. The laws that God used to create the universe, life and people are *not* the same as the natural laws that are now in operation. The founders of scientific method were aware of this and laid down that *primary causes* (how the universe and everything in it came into being) must be separated from *secondary causes* (how the universe works now). Scientific method is about secondary causes—we are in no position to observe and study primary causes. This explains why we have to rely on the Bible for the explanation of origins; the laws by which God created are entirely outside the realm of scientific method. This also explains why, when origins are examined scientifically, scientific method cannot be applied, because we are studying primary causes. Additionally, this explains why any conclusions that we reach appear to be anti-evolution and actually conclude *nothing* about creation as such. It is not really possible to apply scientific method to the study of origins, because, when we do so, we find that it can only be applied to secondary causes, and we end up concluding that evolution is unscientific and cannot be a secondary cause—that is, evolution cannot be an explanation for how God sustains life on earth and causes it to develop the way it has.

The universe was created by a God of reason. We find reason from beginning to end in the Bible. Throughout the Bible, God argues rationally with humans: he tells us *what* we should and should not do, and *why* we should and should not do it. He also teaches cause and effect in human and divine relationships. Belief in a rational universe is part and parcel of scientific method, because the scientists who developed scientific method believed that the Bible was the book of God's words, and they believed that God's works (that is, the natural world which they believed was God's creation) should be examined with the same reverence with which they studied God's Word. They found reason in the Bible and believed that they would find reason in the natural world. And they did! They were therefore able to build up rational systems (for example, laws) on the basis of a uniform and orderly creation. They did not try to impose their systems on the natural world, as ancient philosophers had done; instead they learnt through the experimental method the way in which one part of nature relates to another.

The Goldilocks effect

I am sure that you are familiar with the story of Goldilocks and the three bears. Remember how Goldilocks found that the baby bear's porridge, chair and bed were *just right*? Well, one thing that baffles the natural-thinking scientist and yet makes a lot of sense to the Christian is the fact that the universe appears to be *just right* for the existence of people. This is now called the 'Goldilocks effect'.

For example, Robert Matthews, Visiting Reader at the Department of Information Engineering at the University of Aston, asked, 'Why, for instance, is our Universe and its laws just right for the existence of life? Some argue that it is because it was specially made for us by a benevolent creator.'[24] It would appear that scientists are perplexed by a string of what they consider to be apparent accidents or coincidences that seem just too improbable to dismiss. Many of the familiar structures of the physical world—atoms, molecules in living systems, stars, galaxies—are remarkably sensitive to the precise value of the physical constants and the form of the fundamental laws of physics. It has been found that the slightest shift in the values of the parameters that are found in nature would bring about a drastic and catastrophic change in the orderliness of the cosmos. It seems as though the numbers that we find in the natural world are finely tuned to make the whole cosmos work properly—just as you would expect if you believed that the cosmos was created by a Creator.

Consider, for example, the structure of the atomic nucleus, where the protons and neutrons are bound tightly together by a strong nuclear force. A small percentage decrease in the strength of this force would have a catastrophic result on the entire universe. Deuterium is an isotope of hydrogen that has one proton and one neutron in its nucleus—hydrogen has just one proton. If there was a reduction in the strength of the strong nuclear force, then the proton and neutron in the nucleus of the deuterium atom would become unstuck and so the sun (and all the other stars, for that matter) would not be able to burn, because deuterium is an important element in its fuel chain. A small percentage increase in the nuclear force would have a worse catastrophic effect, for it would be possible for two protons to stick together, which would mean that the universe would be denuded of free protons, with the result that there would be little or no hydrogen in the universe. If there was no hydrogen, there would be no water. Also, if there was no hydrogen, there would be no life on the earth, for the chemicals that are found in living systems contain hydrogen. Furthermore, if there was no hydrogen, there would be no sun or stars, because hydrogen is the basic fuel that causes them to burn. God in his wisdom, however, created the universe with all the parameters finely balanced so that the earth would be a suitable place for us to inhabit. No wonder that, when God saw all that he had created, he pronounced it to be 'very good' (Gen. 1:31).

There is more to be said about the Goldilocks effect. The earth's distance from the sun is just right for us to live comfortably. If the earth was just a few million miles further away from the sun, the earth would be in a permanent deep freeze, with no life existing on it. If, on the other hand, it was a few million miles nearer to the sun, all life on the earth would fry to death. The earth is in the Goldilocks zone, where it is *just right* for all life forms to live comfortably. The fact that we have such a large moon orbiting our earth also sustains life on the earth. If we did not have the moon, we would not have tides; and if we did not have tides, the seas and the oceans would stagnate, leaving them unable to sustain life. The size of the moon also helps sustain life on earth, as pointed out in an article in a *New Scientist Special* on the solar system:

Such a big moon is a big boon for life. As Earth spins on its axis, it has a natural tendency to wobble, owing to that varying pull on it from other bodies such as the Sun. The unseen hand of the moon's gravity gently damps that wobble, preventing rotational instability which would otherwise have caused dramatic changes in Earth's climatic zones over time.[25]

Finally, the position of the solar system in the Milky Way galaxy is also in the Goldilocks zone because its location is out of the way of the galaxy's dangerous spiral arms, which are composed of millions of stars, and therefore is not exposed to disruptive gravitational forces or too much radiation. When God created everything, he not only put the earth in the Goldilocks zone (the habitable zone of the solar system), he also put the solar system in the Goldilocks zone of the Milky Way. He did this in order for life to be able to exist on this planet, as is confirmed in the Scriptures: 'For thus saith the LORD that created the heavens; God himself that formed the earth and made it; he hath established it, he created it not in vain, he formed it to be inhabited: I am the LORD; and there is none else' (Isa. 45:18, KJV).

Although the Bible does not mention the Goldilocks effect, it does confirm that the purpose of the universe and of the earth is to sustain life.

Conclusion

In this chapter, our journey into space has confirmed two things. The first is that Haldane's famous statement is true: the universe is indeed stranger than we suppose. The second is that, when we look at the size of the universe and the great number and variety of stars that we find in it, we are able to declare with the psalmist, 'The heavens declare the glory of God' (Ps. 19:1).

We have looked carefully at the widely accepted view concerning the origin of the universe—the Big Bang—and have seen that this hypothesis is not scientific and is riddled with problems. We have seen that the idea of multiverses is not based on scientific endeavour but is the figment of the imagination of those astronomers who propose it. We have also seen that the universe is understandable, and that this is because we humans are made in the image and likeness of the God who has created us. Finally, we saw that we have to thank God for putting us in the Goldilocks zone, not only in the solar system, but also in the Milky Way galaxy. If we were not in this habitable zone in both the solar system and the Milky Way galaxy, life on earth would not exist.

A whole section in this chapter was devoted to the *origin* of the universe. But what about its *future*? What, if anything, do we know about that? Evolutionary scientists believe that one day the universe will experience what they call a 'heat death', although in reality it should be called a 'cold death', for they consider that the temperature of the universe will be just a fraction of a degree above absolute zero. This will happen, so they believe, when all the energy that is available to do work will have been used up, and nothing will happen any more—the universe will just 'be'. The time period for when the universe will supposedly reach this state is almost unimaginable. It is thought that it will take about one trillion years for all the stars to use up all their fuel and fizzle out. By then, of course, there will be no life left in the universe; every single life form, including humans, will have become extinct billions of years previously. There will still, however, be occasional flashes of starlight in the dark universe, as very large stars collapse in on themselves to form black holes. For the next 10^{122} (the figure 1 followed by 122 zeros!) years, this 'Hawking Radiation' will be the only thing happening in the universe. Then, when all the black holes have evaporated, there will be darkness for 10^{26} years, during which time the universe will simply 'be' and nothing will happen.

This depressing view of the future is in complete contrast with what the Bible teaches. Scripture says that, in contrast to this cold death, the entire universe will be consumed by a real heat death: 'But the day of the Lord will come as a thief in the night, in which the heavens will pass away with a great noise, and the elements will melt with fervent heat; both the earth and the works that are in it will be burned up' (2 Peter 3:10).

The universe will not last for eons, slowly running down. The Bible teaches that one day (and we must remember that no one, only God the Father, knows when that day will be—Matt. 24:36) the Lord will return and the universe, including the earth, will then suffer a catastrophic heat death which will annihilate the present cosmos. God will then create a new heavens and a new earth as described by the apostle John in Revelation 21. We should not view this future event light-heartedly or matter-of-factly, for the apostle Peter uses these events to warn us that we should live our lives in 'holy conduct and godliness' (2 Peter 3:11). Although the apostle Paul tells us in 1 Corinthians 2:9 that we really do not have any idea about how wonderful heaven will be, the apostle John had a vision of heaven, and he told us that there 'God will wipe away every tear from their eyes; there shall be no more death, nor sorrow, nor crying. There shall be no more pain, for the former things have passed away' (Rev. 21:4).

Notes

1 **Isaac Asimov,** *Science Digest,* vol. 69 (April 1971), p. 69.

2 **D. E. Thomson,** 'The Majestic, Unfathomable Universe', in *Science News*, 104/7–8 (August 1973), p. 112.

3 **J. B. S. Haldane,** 'Possible Worlds', in *Possible Worlds and Other Essays* (London: Chatto & Windus, 1927), p. 286.

4 I have deliberately used miles as a measure of distance. To convert miles into kilometres, multiply them by 1.67. A light year is 6 trillion miles, or 10 trillion kilometres. Furthermore, I have used the scientifically accepted nomenclature for million, billion, trillion, and so on— that is, 10^6 is a million; 10^9 is a billion; 10^{12} is a trillion; 10^{15} is a quadrillion; 10^{18} is a quintillion; 10^{21} is a sextillion; 10^{24} is a septillion; and so on.

5 Betelgeuse is the red star that is found in the top left-hand corner of the constellation Orion, which is visible in the winter months in the Northern Hemisphere.

6 'Astronomers Find Evidence for Tens of Thousands of Black Holes', 11 January 2005, at: sciencedaily.com.

7 **Heather Couper** and **Nigel Henbest,** *Big Bang* (New York: DK Publishing, 1997), p. 8.

8 **David Darling,** 'On Creating Something From Nothing', in *New Scientist*, vol. 151 (14 September 1996), p. 46.

9 Quoted by **Marcus Chown** in *The Never-Ending Days of Being Dead* (London: Faber & Faber, 2007), pp. 162–163.

10 Ibid. p. 162.

11 Cited in **Chown,** *The Never-Ending Days of Being Dead*, pp. 56–58.

12 **Peter Coles,** *Cosmology: A Very Short Introduction* (Oxford: Oxford University Press, 2001), p. 44.

13 Quantum theory suggests that energy exists in discrete units called 'quanta'.

14 **E. Learner et al.,** 'An Open Letter to the Scientific Community', in *New Scientist*, vol. 182 (22 May 2004), p. 20; at: cosmologystatement.org.

15 **A. A. Penzias** and **R. W. Wilson,** *Astrophysical Journal*, vol. 142 (1965), p. 419.

16 **Sir Arthur Eddington,** *The Internal Constitution of the Stars* (Cambridge: Cambridge University Press, 1926).

17 **Karen Fox,** *The Big Bang Theory: What It Is, Where It Came From, and Why It Works* (New York: John Wiley & Sons, 2002), p. 134.

18 Taken from **Jason Lisle,** 'Does the Big Bang Fit with the Bible?', in **Ken Ham,** (ed.), *The New Answers Book 2* (Green Forest, AR: Master Books, 2008), pp. 55–62.

19 Quoted by **Dennis Overbye** in 'A New View of Our Universe: Only One of Many', 29 October 2002, at: nytimes.com.

20 **Marcus Chown,** *The Never-Ending Days of Being Dead* (London: Faber & Faber, 2007), p. 3.

21 Ibid.

22 One of the truly great science-fiction short stories about a man transferring to a parallel universe is **John Wyndham's** 'Random Quest', included in his collection of short stories entitled *Consider Her Ways and Others* (London: Penguin, 1965).

23 Quoted by **Marcus Chown,** 'Was the Universe Created by Angels?', 5 June 2007, at: popularscience.co.uk.

24 **Robert Matthews,** 'The Cosmos Next Door', in *BBC Focus Magazine* (December 2003), p. 63.

25 **Marcus Chown,** 'Why are the Sun and Moon the Same Size in the Sky?', in *New Scientist Unknown Solar System Special* (31 January 2009), p. 28.

The origin of life

The formation of living organisms from non-living substances is called 'abiogenesis'. The expression that is used to describe the supposed evolution of living organisms from non-life chemicals is 'chemical evolution'. Strictly speaking, however, chemical evolution is the term that is used to describe the chemical events that supposedly took place on the hypothetical pre-biotic earth that finally led to the appearance of the first living cell. According to chemical evolutionists (those who study these processes), the evolution of non-life into life took place over a period of about one billion years, some 4,500 to 3,500 million years ago.

Chemical evolutionists believe that the atmosphere of the pre-biotic earth was very different from that which we have today. They believe that this atmosphere was subjected to external forces, such as the sun's radiation and cosmic ray bombardment, as well as internal effects, such as thunder storms with their associated electrical discharges (in the form of lightning). As a result, chemical evolutionists believe that the simple inorganic compounds in that atmosphere reacted together and formed, among other things, simple organic compounds called amino acids.

Amino acids are the basic building blocks of proteins, which, in turn, are the building blocks of living things. Chemical evolutionists believe that, as well as amino acids, other chemicals that are found in living organisms also formed—chemicals such as sugars and compounds called nucleic acid bases, which are the building blocks of DNA. Chemical evolutionists then argue that these newly formed chemicals fell into the earth's primeval ocean over a period of hundreds of millions of years and eventually gave rise to a solution of organic matter which is commonly referred to as the 'primeval soup'.

Chemical evolutionists would have us believe that these basic organic compounds then assembled themselves, in the course of time and by chance natural processes, into rather complex organic compounds which were capable of self-replicating—that is, capable of producing exact copies of themselves. We are told that these compounds eventually assembled themselves, again by chance, into a living cell. It must be remembered, however, that the simplest living cell is incredibly complex—even more complex than the largest modern industrial manufacturing plant, with all its suppliers, sub-contractors and retailers as well as accountants. It is this enormous gap between the simple organic compounds and a living cell that is bridged by the chemical evolutionists' speculations regarding the chance natural processes in the primeval soup. In other words, their speculations are designed to explain, in evolutionary terms, the origin of life itself.

It should be noted, however, that, at the time of writing, no one has yet synthesized anything remotely resembling a living cell in the laboratory. Using the basic components which chemical evolutionists maintain would have been present in the primeval soup, scientists have not been able to synthesize what might be called a 'proto-cell' which has some basic properties of life. Without such a 'proof of principle', explanations for the origin of life from non-life tend to be short on specifics, as we shall see.

No intelligence necessary?

One of the problems that we may face when we consider chemical evolution is that we are struggling with chemical names and chemical processes that are unfamiliar to us. This can sometimes confuse us and lead us to think that, because it is chemistry, these things can and will happen. In this chapter, we will see that the probability of natural processes alone producing a living organism from non-living chemicals is zero. However, evolutionists say that, since we are here, it must have happened in the way they describe—by chance natural processes without the intervention of any supernatural agent whatsoever. Because of this, we are sometimes tempted to believe that chemical evolution *has* taken place. But what if I asked you to believe that a completed jigsaw was the result of my throwing all the pieces of the jigsaw up into the air and their landing on the table in their correct positions, without the intervention of any intelligent dexterous person? You would not believe it, and quite right, too! So why are we tempted to believe the fairy stories of chemical evolutionists?

Interestingly, the philosophy of the chemical evolutionists can be summed up as follows. They think that, if they can synthesize life in the laboratory, they will have proven that no intelligence was necessary to form life on the pre-biotic earth. They seem to forget that, if they *make* a self-replicating system or living organism in their laboratories, it will have been as a result of *their own cleverness*. Their *intelligence* would have been responsible for the outcome of the experiment—from the design of the apparatus, the chemicals used in the experiment, the temperature and pressure under which the chemicals react and so on. However, they think that their carefully designed experiments reflect the random conditions that are supposed to have existed on the earth billions of years ago. They also believe that their carefully designed experiments reflect the chance natural processes that supposedly occurred on the hypothetical pre-biotic earth.

Undeterred, chemical evolutionists refer to one of the most famous chemical evolution experiments that has ever been carried out—famous, because it was the first. In 1953, Stanley Miller performed an experiment in the laboratory that allegedly showed that life had indeed evolved from non-life chemicals on the hypothetical pre-biotic earth.[1] Miller circulated a mixture of methane, ammonia, hydrogen and water vapour around an apparatus that had two important components. The first was an electrical-discharge chamber—a place where the gases were subject to high-energy radiation. The other was a cold trap—a place where any organic compounds that formed in the electrical-discharge chamber could be trapped out and so could no longer be involved in the experiment. After circulating the gases for about a week, Miller showed that he had produced a mixture of amino acids—glycine, α- and β-alanine, aspartic acid and α-amino-butyric acid. Some sugars, lipids, and some of the building blocks for nucleic acids were also formed. As amino acids are the building blocks of proteins, and as proteins are the building blocks of living systems, this experiment was hailed as proof that life had arisen from non-life chemicals on the hypothetical pre-biotic earth.

Since Stanley Miller's experiment, other chemical evolutionists have manufactured, under a variety of conditions and using various gases, a variety of amino acids and sugars as well as other compounds that are found in living systems. Evolutionists have generally accepted these results uncritically, hailing them as incontrovertible evidence that life arose from non-life chemicals in the hypothetical pre-biotic earth's 'primeval soup' billions of years ago.

These experiments, however, *do not* prove that chemical evolution occurred. All that such experiments show is that, under certain conditions, inorganic compounds can be converted into organic compounds—nothing more, nothing less! Furthermore, it can be shown that these experiments have nothing to do with the origin of life as they do *not* reflect the conditions that are thought to have existed on the hypothetical pre-biotic earth. In the next three sections of this chapter, we shall look carefully at this. In the first section we shall see why the construction of the apparatus used by Miller does not reflect the configuration of the atmosphere, and why the gases in the apparatus did not reflect the composition of the earth's pre-biotic atmosphere as proposed by the chemical evolutionists. In the second section we shall consider the problems of synthesizing proteins. Then, in the third section, we shall look at the so-called 'handedness' of the amino acids and the nucleic acid sugars that we find in living systems.

The earth's atmosphere

The first problem with Miller's experiment is that the amino acids that were formed in the reaction chamber, where the gases were bombarded with high-energy radiation, were removed by means of a cold trap. This, however, does not reflect the configuration of the earth's atmosphere. The earth's atmosphere does *not* have any such cold trap anywhere you care to look—either today or in the past, for that matter. There is nowhere where any simple organic compounds that exist (or have existed) in the atmosphere can be removed by being 'frozen out' by a cold trap. All the gases that are found in the atmosphere form a homogeneous mixture with no mechanism for any of the gases to be frozen out and therefore removed.

Because of the absence of such a cold trap in the atmosphere, the formation of simple organic compounds, such as amino acids, would not occur as readily as it does in laboratory experiments such as Miller's. The reason for this is that the ultra-violet radiation which causes the amino acids to form from the methane-ammonia-hydrogen-water-vapour mixture also causes their decomposition. This means that, as soon as the amino acids form, they would begin to be destroyed by the ultra-violet radiation. In laboratory experiments, this problem is overcome by the use of a cold trap which immediately removes the newly formed organic compounds out of the system, thus preventing their decomposition. Such a cold trap was not present on the hypothetical pre-biotic earth, hence any organic compounds that formed in the hypothetical atmosphere of the supposed pre-biotic earth would soon have been destroyed.

There is yet another problem with the hypothetical pre-biotic atmosphere. Its proposed composition is based upon the argument that this atmosphere must have been *reducing*; this means that it contained no oxygen. This is because it is impossible to produce the organic compounds that are found in living organisms in what is called an *oxidizing* atmosphere—that is, one in which oxygen is present. Initially, the idea that the hypothetical pre-biotic earth's atmosphere was oxygen-free and composed of methane, ammonia, hydrogen and water vapour was widely accepted by chemical evolutionists. Recently, however, doubts have been expressed about this proposed composition of the earth's pre-biotic atmosphere: 'It is widely accepted that the gases Miller used did not accurately recreate conditions on early Earth—carbon dioxide and nitrogen were probably the main components of the atmosphere.'[2]

In fact, there does not seem to be any agreement among chemical evolutionists concerning the composition of the pre-biotic earth's atmosphere; opinions vary from 'reducing' (that is, an atmosphere either composed of methane, nitrogen, ammonia and water vapour or of carbon dioxide, hydrogen and nitrogen) to 'neutral' (that is, an atmosphere composed of carbon dioxide, nitrogen and water vapour).[3] Other chemical evolutionists have suggested that the atmosphere was rich in carbon monoxide and sulfur compounds (such as hydrogen sulfide) as a result of volcanic eruptions taking place on the supposed pre-biotic earth.[4] Other chemical evolutionists, however, have proposed that the atmosphere was rich in hydrogen cyanide.[5]

The one thing that is common to all these proposals, however, is that, in order to synthesize organic compounds from any of the mixtures of gases that are proposed by chemical evolutionists, *oxygen must be absent*. When oxygen gas is added to any of these mixtures, no organic molecules are formed. Herein lies a conundrum. When oxygen is present, no organic compounds are formed. However, on the hypothetical pre-biotic earth, if oxygen was absent, the ozone layer would not have formed. If there was no ozone layer, there would have been no protection from the sun's ultra-violet radiation that causes organic compounds (particularly amino acids) to decompose quickly. Hence the conundrum for chemical evolutionists is this: with oxygen, organic compounds do not get synthesized; without oxygen, the organic compounds that are formed decompose quickly, so no organic compounds remain.

There is, however, no geochemical evidence for an atmosphere with the composition used in Miller's experiment ever having existed on the earth—in fact, there is much evidence against it. One factor is that large quantities of hydrophobic organic compounds would have been formed by the irradiation of the large amounts of methane supposedly present in the pre-biotic atmosphere. These compounds would have been absorbed by the sedimentary clays being deposited at the time. The supposedly early rocks should therefore contain large quantities of organic compounds— but they do not! In fact, the iron-ore bodies found in the supposedly ancient Pre-Cambrian rocks are oxidized, showing that the atmosphere of the earth was oxidizing (it contained oxygen) when these bodies formed—a time when the atmosphere should have been reducing (i.e. oxygen-free) according to chemical evolutionists. Furthermore, the presence of uranium in sediments in the Pre-Cambrian rocks indicates that it was transported in solution by oxygenated water—otherwise it would have precipitated out. It turns out that all the geological evidence suggests that all sedimentary rocks were deposited on an earth which had an atmosphere with a similar composition to the one that exists now.

There are also three additional problems concerning the composition of the earth's hypothetical primitive atmosphere as proposed by Miller. Firstly, the reducing nature of the atmosphere would very soon disappear, due to oxygen being formed as the water vapour was decomposed by the ultra-violet radiation coming from the sun. Secondly, the ammonia would be completely disintegrated by the ultra-violet radiation in about 30,000 years, yet a billion years is required for chemical evolution to occur. Thirdly, because of their lightness, large amounts of the hydrogen and methane would be lost to space very quickly—certainly in less than a billion years. Hence the composition of this hypothetical atmosphere would have changed very quickly—it certainly would not have remained essentially the same for the billion years needed for the formation of the organic compounds required for chemical evolution to have occurred.

A dry soup?

It is very illuminating to look at the mechanisms proposed by chemical evolutionists in order to build from amino acids to proteins to self-replicating systems to living cells. Proteins are polymers of amino acids; in other words, a protein consists of many different amino acids joined together. It turns out that proteins are quite difficult to synthesize from their amino acid constituents. In the 1960s, the famous chemical evolutionist Sydney Fox managed to polymerize amino acids in his laboratory by heating a mixture of *dry* amino acids at 175°C for six hours.[6] When water was added and the resulting mixture allowed to cool down, the polymers formed spherical globules or micro-spheres. Although these micro-spheres have properties similar to proteins, they are not proteins, but are called 'protenoids'. Incredibly, Sydney Fox concluded that, as a result of such an experiment, the problem of how the first primitive cell could have arisen had been solved! However, the creationist Duane Gish has pointed out that there is an enormous difference between one of these so-called 'Fox's micro-spheres' and a simple living cell: 'Their contents, however, can consist only of random polymers of amino acids. There can be no information content nor information transfer systems, no organized elements, no enzymes, no coenzymes, no energy-forming systems or energy-utilizing systems, certainly no nucleic acids, no replicating system, in fact, they can contain nothing but a mixture of random polymers of amino acids.'[7]

When we consider the results of Fox's experiments and the plausibility of such reactions having occurred naturalistically in the hypothetical primeval soup on the pre-biotic earth, we are faced with a number of problems. The *first* problem is that the temperature required (175° C) is well above the boiling point of water (100°C) and well above the boiling point of the hypothetical primeval soup. In order to overcome this problem, it has been suggested that a temperature of 175°C or so would have been found on the edges of volcanoes and that this is where the evolution of living structures from simple amino acids occurred. But this raises another problem, as we shall see later.

The *second* problem is that in Fox's experiments *pure*, *dry* amino acids were used. In the hypothetical primeval soup, however, the amino acid mixture would not have been pure—the amino acids would have been contaminated with other organic (and even inorganic) compounds which would have prevented any polymerization taking place. Furthermore, it cannot be overemphasized that conditions have to be *dry*. How it is possible to have dry conditions in a primeval soup is beyond imagination—unless, of course, it is included in one of those six impossible things that the Queen thought about before breakfast in Lewis Carroll's *Alice in Wonderland*. Dry conditions would certainly not be present in the primeval soup which was 99 per cent water, according to chemical evolutionists! Even if these reactions occurred at the edges of volcanoes (as, we have seen, is suggested by chemical evolutionists), dry conditions would still be difficult to find as volcanic gases often contain up to 70 per cent water. It is interesting to note that, if water is included in the laboratory experiments, a charred mess, not proteins, is the end product.

The *third* problem is that in laboratory experiments, a high proportion of glutamic and aspartic acids or of lysine has to be used in order to get the amino acids to polymerize. These compounds would not necessarily have been present in such high proportions on the hypothetical pre-biotic earth.

The *fourth* and final problem is that, in order for polymerization to occur, an energy source is required—that is, heat. Now, the problem of heat is twofold: firstly, many amino acids are destroyed by heat; and secondly, proteins are destroyed by heat. So this problem can be summarized as follows: without heat, the amino acids will not polymerize and form proteins; with heat, the amino acids are destroyed and any proteins that form are also destroyed. The end result is the same: no heat, no proteins; heat, no proteins!

Origin of life and probability

But there is yet another problem with the hypothesis of life having originated by chance natural processes from lifeless organic molecules, and this can be seen by using the laws of probability, because the frequency of occurrence of any given amino acid in naturally occurring protein chains which have been sequentially analysed has been shown to be random.[8]

Let us suppose that we have twenty different amino acids and from these we wish to construct *by chance* one molecule of a small protein that is 100 amino acids long and has a particular amino acid sequence. There are 20^{100} or 10^{130} possible different configurations of this protein. Now let us suppose that the primeval soup contained only these twenty different amino acids. The chance of this protein molecule forming in the hypothetical primeval soup is 1 in 10^{130} (which is 1 followed by 130 zeros 10,000,000,000,000,000,000,000,000,000,000,000,000,000,000,000,000,000, 000,000,000,000,000,000,000,000,000,000,000,000,000,000,000,000,000, 000,000,000,000,000,000,000,000,000,000). To give you some idea of how enormous this number is, it is estimated that there are something like 10^{80} atoms in the universe. The number 10^{130} is actually the number of atoms that would exist in 10^{50} or 100,000,000,000,000,000,000,000,000,000,000, 000,000,000,000,000,000 universes! The probability of this protein molecule forming by chance is therefore, to all intents and purposes, zero. Yet despite such overwhelming odds against protein formation from amino acids having occurred by chance in the primeval soup, chemical evolutionists still maintain that it happened.

A similar result on the hypothesis that the origin of life originated by chance is obtained by the use of information theory. Information theory is the quantitive study of the transmission of information. In an article entitled 'Reflections of a Communication Engineer', Marcel Golay wrote,

Suppose we wanted to build a machine capable of reaching into bins for all of its parts, and capable of assembling from these parts a second machine, just like itself. What is the minimum amount of structure or information which should be built into the first machine? The answer came out to be of the order of 1500 bits—1500 choices between alternatives which the machine should be able to decide. This answer is very suggestive, because 1500 bits happens to be also the order of magnitude of the amount of structure contained in the simplest large protein molecule which, immersed in a bath of nutrients, can induce the assembly of these nutrients into another large protein molecule like itself, and then separate itself from it. That is what the process called life consists of, and unless and until we discover a new process in which simpler molecules have semi-life properties, the inquiry into the birth of life can be reduced to an inquiry into the possibility or probability of the spontaneous assembly of such a molecule, out of a bath of its essential constituents.[9]

Golay then went on to show that, by making the most favourable assumptions regarding the conditions under which the spontaneous generation of life is thought to have occurred, the chemical evolutionist can only account for 150 of the 1,500 bits. These bits can be represented numerically as 2^{150} and 2^{1500} respectively. The number 2^{150} is 10^{450} (that is, the figure 1 followed by 450 zeros). Even when this number is divided by the number of stars in the universe (10^{22}), which is the number of the potential solar systems, the number obtained is 10^{428} (that is, the figure 1 followed by 428 zeros). Hence, by applying information theory to chemical evolution, it can be seen that the chance of life originating spontaneously anywhere in the universe is in the order of 10^{428} to 1 against. This number is again, to all intents and purposes, zero.

Calculations such as these show that the probability of life having originated by chance is virtually zero. Evolutionists, however, argue that, since we are here, it must have happened in the way they propose, no matter how small the probability. It is my strong conviction that chemical evolutionists cling to chance random processes as the mechanism whereby life originated because the idea of an Almighty God who is the Creator of life is repugnant to them.

Is God left-handed?

Chemical evolutionists are confronted not only with the problems arising from the proposed composition of the earth's pre-biotic atmosphere, but also with the problem that such a proposed composition would ensure that an infinite number of amino acids would have formed. Yet only twenty amino acids are found as the basic building blocks of the naturally occurring proteins. Chemical evolutionists have no adequate explanations as to why only these twenty are found.

There is yet another problem that faces chemical evolutionists as they consider these twenty amino acids that are used as the basic building blocks of naturally occurring proteins. This problem is known as 'chirality'. Every amino acid (except glycine) found in the proteins that exist in living organisms can exist in two forms, each one being the mirror image of the other. These two forms have the same relationship to each other that the right hand has to the left hand—they are mirror images that cannot be superimposed. As they have the same spatial relationship as hands, one is arbitrarily called 'right-handed' or 'D' (from the Latin *dexter* meaning 'right') and the other 'left-handed' or 'L' (from the Latin *laevus* meaning 'left'). This classification is purely spatial, for the two forms are indistinguishable, having exactly the same chemical composition and properties, and exactly the same physical properties, such as melting point and solubility.

It has been found, however, that all the amino acids that are found in the proteins that exist in living organisms are of the L, or left-handed, variety. The D, or right-handed, amino acids are not found in living systems. This has actually caused some to wonder whether God is left-handed![10] This use of L amino acids in the proteins found in living systems is a problem to chemical evolutionists, because the formation of the amino acids from inorganic substances in laboratory experiments always produces both D *and* L forms of amino acids in equal proportions. Hence the hypothetical primeval soup would have contained both the D and L forms of amino acids in equal proportions. Chemical evolutionists are unable to explain why it is that only the L form of amino acids is found in the proteins of living organisms. They cannot envisage a mechanism whereby only L amino acids are 'used' for protein synthesis in preference to the D forms. As the D and L forms would have been present in equal proportions in the hypothetical primeval soup, both forms should be found in proteins, but they are not—only the L forms are present.

The form of amino acids used in protein synthesis also determines the overall shape of the protein. Naturally-occurring proteins exist as an α-helix. This is because the L forms of amino acids are used to build the protein. If only D forms were used, the protein would be the mirror image of the one containing only L forms. If D and L forms were linked up randomly, the protein would have no helical shape and would exist as a long 'floppy' chain. Again, chemical evolutionists are unable to explain why such floppy-chain proteins are not found in nature, as they should be if chemical evolution occurred.

To complicate matters even further, chemical evolutionists must also explain why it is only the D forms of the nucleic-acid sugars (ribose and deoxyribose) that are found in living organisms. If chemical evolution occurred, both the D and L forms of the nucleic-acid sugars should be found in living systems, because both forms would have been formed in the hypothetical primeval soup. But the L forms are conspicuously absent. If the L forms were found in equal proportion to the D forms (as one would expect if living systems evolved from the chemical evolutionists' hypothetical primeval soup, which would have contained the D and the L forms in equal proportions), the structure of DNA, for example, would not have the beautiful double-helix structure that it has, but would be irregular. If it had such an irregular structure, it would not be able to self-replicate as it does.

It has been suggested that the specific 'handedness' of the amino acids in living proteins is due to the fact that the first proteins that were used in living systems formed on clays. The reason for this is that experiments performed in the laboratory using clays as a medium for the synthesis of proteins from 50/50 left-/right-handed amino acids have shown a slight predisposition (or bias) towards the left-handed amino acids being used to form the proteins. However, even if modern clays (like those used in laboratory experiments) do have such a bias towards one form of handedness over another, this is due to the contamination by optically active biomolecules produced by living systems that are alive today, and also by life forms that lived in the past (when the clay was forming). This would mean that clays that existed before there was life on the earth would not have had the bias that is observed in the laboratory experiments.

There is, in fact, no structural reason for selecting organic compounds of one type of 'handedness' rather than the other. Nor is there any convincing argument that explains why all amino acids in proteins have the same configuration. Nor is there any explanation for the fact that it is only the D forms of naturally occurring sugars that are found in living organisms. Nor is it understood why L amino acids, rather than D amino acids, are associated with D nucleic-acid sugars. Perhaps the fact that only the L forms of amino acids and the D forms of nucleic-acid sugars are found in living organisms means that God is not left-handed at all—maybe it shows that he is ambidextrous!

Monkeys and typewriters

Before we look at the results of the experiments performed by our simian friends on computer keyboards, let us remind ourselves that the chemical instructions for the construction of a human being exist in every fertilized egg. The amount of information in the chromosomes of a fertilized human egg is equivalent to a library of about 5,520 books, each 250 pages long (assuming about 350 words per page). Thus each human male's sperm and each human female's ovum functions like a miniaturized library filled with written chemical instructions to build a human being. In fact, every fertilized egg of any living organism (plant or animal) contains the chemical instructions to construct that particular living organism.

For evolutionists, this chemical writing on the genes is no proof at all that it has been written, designed or developed by a Creator. For them, the laws of nature and the properties of matter wrote and 'designed' everything—a Creator had nothing at all to do with it whatsoever! Creationists are considered to be naïve, believing, as they do, in a Divine Author of this chemical writing on the genes. The evolutionists attribute this writing to purely random factors; chance and the laws of nature are considered to be the final cause of the entire genetic code and its chemical projects (that is, living organisms). For them, the entire genetic mechanism, as well as its contents, simply developed because of the laws of nature. For them, the genetic language, with all its grammar and correction mechanisms, developed merely by chance. For them, the chemical instructions to construct eyes, ears, brains, hearts, livers, kidneys, hair, bones, muscles, skin and so on (and the instructions to put them together in an ordered fashion and to make them function in and as a body) developed by purely random processes.

Evolutionists also tell us that chance was sorted by natural selection. It should be noted, however, that natural selection itself can create nothing—it can only sort out that which has supposedly been provided by random natural processes. Yet, in spite of this, belief in a constructive Creator of the body parts found in organisms and the information and code involved with their making and functioning is considered to be totally superfluous by evolutionists. The sugars, the phosphates and the four bases that are the building blocks of DNA (guanine, thymine, cytosine and adenine) supposedly formed the DNA molecule (in helical form) under the influence of the laws of nature present in all matter. At the same time—or with time—the grammar and punctuation of the genetic language is supposed to have developed randomly, guided by the same laws of nature.

Chance and the laws of nature then supposedly provided plans for organs such as eyes, ears, brains (which can be considered as electronically based computers with millions of switching mechanisms to provide intelligence, consciousness and memory); for hearts (which are capable of pumping blood continuously for periods exceeding seventy years, while simultaneously undergoing repair processes); for livers; for kidneys; for hair, bones, muscles, skin and so on. Additionally, these chance processes are said to have provided plans for nerve endings to equip organisms with taste and sensation such as touch; for tongues and vocal chords to speak (plus a mini-computer to control the tongue and coordinate speech); for cells that produce blood; for digestive systems, which at a slightly elevated temperature break down food (which can be considered to be fats, carbohydrates and proteins) into their constituents; for repair mechanisms to heal wounds—in brief, all the know-how to produce and maintain a complex living organism. All this, according to evolutionists, developed by itself through purely random processes.

Now, if this is so, the laws of thermodynamics must be in error. These laws show that matter has neither project-content nor teleology—that is, a goal-directed activity. Because humans, animals and plants are biological machines built by means of a programmed language, the questions that we must ask are: If matter is agitated, will it build a machine? Can chance alone plan and construct a machine? Can randomness devise a meaningful language? Can chance, collaborating with the non-teleological laws of nature, have built any teleological machine or programme?

In reality, evolutionists are asking us to believe that the paper on which the text of a book is written developed not only the language in which the book is written, but also all its concepts, ideas, and thoughts—in other words, that the paper wrote the entire book! Creationists, on the other hand, believe in an Author who wrote the book of life—just as any other book, without exception, has been written by an author and not by the paper on which it is written! Life consists of various genetic books—a different genetic book for each kind of life. Although the genetic language (the genetic code) is identical in all forms of life, the content varies according to the kind of life. This explains the fact that, although organisms as different as daffodils, lettuces, mice, chimpanzees and humans have the same genetic code, they differ from one another genetically. Humans and chimpanzees share 96 per cent of their genes; humans and mice 80 per cent; humans and lettuce 40 per cent; and humans and daffodils 35 per cent (that's one for all us Welsh people to contemplate). Both similarities and differences in these organisms can be explained because the genetic language is identical in all these organisms but the content varies, according to the kind of life. This does not prove evolution; rather it points to a Creator who always employed the same language to store and realize his ideas, projects and life concepts. Creationists therefore regard their belief in a Creator to be rational and also experimentally justifiable.

From a study of the information found in DNA, Dr Werner Gitt, an expert in information systems, has concluded that both chemical and biological evolution is false. His arguments and logical deductions can be summarized as follows:

Since the DNA code has all the essential characteristics of information, there must have been a sender of this information.

Since the density and complexity of the DNA information is millions of times greater than man's present technology, the sender must be supremely intelligent.

Since the sender must have encoded (stored) the information into the DNA molecule and constructed the molecular biomachines to encode, decode and run the cells, the sender must be purposeful and supremely powerful.

Since information is a nonmaterial entity and cannot originate from matter, the sender must have a nonmaterial component (spirit).

Since information cannot originate from matter and is also created by man, man's nature must have a nonmaterial component (spirit).

Since biological information can only originate from an intelligent sender and all theories of chemical and biological evolution are based on the premise that information comes solely from matter and energy (with no sender), then the theories of chemical and biological evolution are false.[11]

As we can see, Dr Gitt's study of the information found in DNA not only shows that chemical evolution is unscientific, but it also leads inevitably to the conclusion that there is a Creator God.

The fundamental question that arises is: Where did the information that is found in living organisms come from? The evolutionists' stock answer is, as we have seen, that it originated by chance. 'Darwin's Bulldog', Thomas Huxley, is often misquoted as having said that, if an infinite number of monkeys tapped away at an infinite number of typewriters, they would eventually produce the complete works of Shakespeare.[12] In order to investigate this hypothesis, students from the University of Plymouth put a computer keyboard in the macaques' enclosure at Paignton Zoo in Devon and let the six inhabitants tap away to their hearts' content. The result of the month-long experiment was that, not only did the monkeys fail to produce one of the Bard's plays, neither did they write a single proper word![13] It could be argued that chemical evolutionists are straining at monkeys and swallowing typewriters (see Matt. 23:24).

Junk yards and jumbo jets

Although I do not agree with all the conclusions reached by E. K. Victor Pearce in his book *Who was Adam?*, he does describe a very amusing analogy that reflects some of the arguments used by chemical evolutionists in their explanation of the origin of life:

When the Melanesian New Stone Age natives were discovered this century [the author is referring to the twentieth century] the natives debated the origin of the white man's goods and aeroplanes. Some tribes were unwilling to believe that the white man had manufactured them in his own factories. They had never seen a factory, so why believe in them? They were also unwilling to think that the white man had outwitted the spirits of their ancestors.

Eventually they hit upon an amusing explanation called 'Cargo', as we shall see, but in order to illustrate our points we shall imagine a conversation which might have ensued between a native and a white man. If the analogy seems ludicrous it should be remembered that it reflects the arguments of some 'Origin of Life' biologists, but stripped of their technical language, which can often hide fallacies. It is also relevant because we now know that the mechanism of life is made of non-living crystals.

A native stands before the airliner—a native who has only recently been introduced to metals and smelting. The white man, impatient at the native's refusal to believe in the white man's aeroplane factories, ironically dismisses the native's curiosity by saying, 'This is how the airliner originated. One day there was a terrific thunderstorm. Lightning played upon ore-bearing rocks, and fused the various ores into lumps of molten iron, copper and bauxite. Again the lightning struck before the metals had cooled, so that the metals formed themselves into patterns inherent in their atomic particles. This resulted in simple components being formed—nuts, bolts, aluminium plates etc. Again the lightning struck and formed more complex components— cylinder heads, pistons, rings, wires (ready insulated), turbines, blades, propeller parts, wheels, and melted some rubber trees into tyres and left all these in a heap.

'Again the lightning struck and flung the heap high into the air. Some of the nuts were near enough to the bolts to respond to an inherent attraction and screw themselves together capturing another component in the process and so were selected for the developing plane. Other pieces fell uselessly as unwanted debris and so were not selected. After repeated lightning the major units were formed: engines, panel instruments, struts, fuselage, tanks, seats and lavatory pans.

'Coincidentally an earthquake ruptured the strata and released oil from an anticline. The oil spouted and poured itself into the tanks, refining and separating into grades on the way.

'A final burst of lightning flung everything up into the air. There were far more parts than those required by any one aeroplane, but those which were lucky enough to fall into a viable position made up a complete airliner which throbbed into life and made a safe landing.'[14]

Although this story is fictitious, what the author is trying to show is that people would rather believe in evolution (the ludicrous story of how the aeroplane came into existence) than believe in God the Creator (the manufacturer of the aeroplane). This same thought was expressed by the late Professor Sir Fred Hoyle and his collaborator Professor Chandra Wickramasinghe of Cardiff University who, after studying the amount of information in the genetic code of living systems, expressed the view that the chances that higher life forms could develop via purely natural processes from non-living chemicals 'is comparable with the chance that a tornado sweeping through a junk-yard might assemble a Boeing 747 from the materials therein ...'[15] I once used this argument when I was giving a lunchtime talk on behalf of the Christian Union in the Biology department at Cardiff University. A research scientist came up to me afterwards and suggested that the formation of a jumbo jet as a result of a tornado going through a junk yard could be achieved if all the pieces of junk in the junk yard *wanted* to become part of a jumbo jet! I was amazed at this suggestion and pointed out to him that pieces of junk are lifeless and therefore do not have desires in the way he had suggested. Although he agreed, this scientist then confessed to me that he believed that every carbon atom in the entire universe *wanted* to become part of an organic molecule that was part of a living system. He told me that he *had* to believe this, because if he did not, he would have to believe in creation and therefore in a Creator God—and he did not want God telling him what to do in his life! I found—and still find—it remarkable that this intelligent research scientist chose to believe such nonsense about carbon atoms having desires and feelings rather than believe in the loving Creator God of the Bible.

Conclusion
The synthesis of amino acids in experiments such as those conducted by Stanley Miller is a long way from the synthesis of the simplest living cell,

comprising, as it does: a membrane that is made in such a way that it is permeable by some substances but not by others; mitochondria, where energy is produced so that the cell can function; ribosomes, which play such an important role in the production of proteins; and a nucleus, with its chromosomes (composed of DNA) which act as a blueprint or master tape so as to ensure that the cell reproduces an exact replica of itself. Finally, the simplest living cell possesses life—that intangible element that presents a problem of such magnitude that chemical evolutionists are unable to give a satisfactory answer to the question of its origin. To believe that life came about by mere chance chemical and physical processes can therefore only be described as an immense exercise of blind faith, contrasted with the rational faith of creationists.

Notes

1 **Stanley L. Miller,** 'A Production of Amino Acids under Possible Primitive Earth Conditions', in *Science,* vol. 117 (1953), pp. 528–529.

2 **Hayley Birch,** 'Stanley Miller's Iconic "Primordial Soup" Experiment Re-examined', in *Chemistry World,* 5/11 (2008), p. 22.

3 **Antonio Lazcano** and **Stanley L. Miller,** 'The Origin and Early Evolution of Life: Prebiotic Chemistry, the Pre-RNA World, and Time', in *Cell,* vol. 85 (14 June 1996), pp. 793–796.

4 See 'Iron–Sulfur World Theory' at: en.wikipedia.org.

5 **J. Oro,** 'Mechanism of Synthesis of Adenine from Hydrogen Cyanide under Possible Primitive Earth Conditions', in *Nature,* vol. 191 (1961), pp. 1193–1194.

6 **Sidney W. Fox,** *Nature,* vol. 205 (1965), p. 328.

7 **Duane T. Gish,** *Speculations and Experiments Related to Theories on the Origin of Life: A Critique* (San Diego: Institute for Creation Research, 1972), p. 30.

8 See **Jacques Monod** and **A. Wainhouse,** (tr.), *Chance and Necessity: An Essay on the Natural Philosophy of Modern Biology* (New York: Alfred A. Knopf, 1971), pp. 94–96.

9 **M. J. E. Golay,** 'Reflections of a Communication Engineer', in *Analytical Chemistry,* 33/7 (1961), pp. 23A–36A.

10 See, for example, **John Noble Wilford,** 'Life's Origin: A Scientist's Search for the Very Beginning', in *New York Times,* 23 February 1982, at: nytimes.com.

11 'Professor Werner Gitt's Conclusions from the Information Found in DNA', from *The Good News,* May/June 2005, at: gnmagazine.org.

12 In 1931, **Sir James Jeans,** in his book *The Mysterious Universe*, attributed this quote to Thomas Huxley, who was supposed to have said it in his famous debate with the Anglican Bishop of Oxford, Samuel Wiberforce, at a meeting of the British Association for the Advancement of Science held on 30 June 1860. However, in 1860, the typewriter itself had yet to emerge!

13 'No Words to Describe Monkeys' Play', 9 May 2003, at: news.bbc.co.uk.

14 E. K. Victor Pearce, *Who Was Adam?* (Exeter: Paternoster, 1969), pp. 103–104.

15 'Hoyle on Evolution', *Nature*, vol. 294 (12 November 1981), p. 105.

The origin of species

No book about origins would be complete without discussing the origin of species. In many people's minds, the word 'evolution' is synonymous with the title of Charles Darwin's book *On the Origin of Species*. For over 150 years—ever since its publication in 1859—this book has been viewed as the evolutionists' Bible. This is strange, really, for Charles Darwin was certainly not the originator of the theory of evolution; evolutionary ideas and interpretations have their roots in the philosophies articulated by the Greeks, Romans, Chinese and Arabs.[1] Evolutionary ideas were, however, increasingly advanced in Europe and the USA in the second half of the eighteenth and the first half of the nineteenth centuries. This has been written about by numerous authors, including Dr Henry Morris, one of the leading creationists of the twentieth century and the founder of the Institute for Creation Research: 'Erasmus Darwin was Charles Darwin's grandfather and was a widely-read and popular writer on evolution even before Charles was born. Wells, Pritchard, and Laurence were all physicians who wrote on evolution and natural selection almost a half-century before *The Origin of Species*. Diderot in France, Edward Blyth in England, and even Benjamin Franklin advanced similar theories.'[2] Dr Morris then noted that Darwin never acknowledged his predecessors and always referred to the origin of species by natural selection as '*my* theory'.

We have already seen that scientists invoke evolutionary ideas when contemplating the origin of the universe and the origin of life. Similarly, when studying the origin of species, scientists (notably biologists and palaeontologists) again turn to evolutionary ideas. Biological evolution could be defined as the development of the first living cell *into* multicellular organisms *into* invertebrates *into* vertebrates *into* amphibians *into* reptiles *into* mammals and finally *into* humans. These events have supposedly stretched over the last 3,500 million years. Biological evolution could therefore be defined as the development from the first living cell into all living and extinct plants and animals, including humans.

Strictly speaking, Darwin's book considered the origin of species *by natural selection*, and it is this phrase which makes it an evolutionary account of the origin of species. Yet, in spite of this, the late Professor Ernst Mayr (an eminent evolutionist) of the University of Harvard was critical of Darwin's thesis: 'Darwin failed to solve the problem indicated by the title to his work. Although he demonstrated the modification of species in the time dimension, he never seriously attempted a rigorous analysis of the problem of the multiplication of species.'[3] A colleague of Mayr's at Harvard, Professor George Gaylord Simpson (another eminent evolutionist), has gone so far as to say that Darwin's 'book called *The Origin of Species* is not really on that subject'![4]

It is not my intention in this section to attack Darwinism as such—this has been done in numerous books and on innumerable websites over the past thirty years. What I intend to do is to look briefly at the life and discoveries of Charles Darwin and to see where he was deluded. During this section, we will start to examine the scientific data offered by scientists in support of the evolution of life on earth. We will continue this examination by looking at the fossil record, for it is here that we should find the evidence for or against biological evolution. We shall also concern ourselves with the proposed mechanism of biological evolution to see to what extent this accounts for the diversity of plant and animal life found on the earth.

Darwin, species and kinds

On 12 February 1809, Charles Darwin was born—hence the worldwide celebrations of the bicentenary of his birth in 2009. To hear and read what has been written and said about this man during the celebrations, one might think that Darwin was the greatest scientist who ever lived. We were confidently told by the media (such as the BBC), by learned scientific societies (such as the Royal Society), by natural-history societies (such as the National Geographic Society) and by scientists (such as Dr Richard Dawkins, Professor Steve Jones and Sir David Attenborough) that Darwin's theory of evolution by means of natural selection explains why we have all the different species of plants and animals on the earth today as well as those of the past that are found in the fossil record. We are also told that Darwin's ideas explain the origin of all the plants and animals, and also why bacteria and viruses become drug resistant.

Darwin was born into a very rich and influential family. His father, Robert, was a GP in Shrewsbury, and he wanted his son, Charles, to follow him into the medical profession. In 1825, therefore, at the age of sixteen, Charles was sent by his father to study Medicine at the University of Edinburgh. In the mid-1820s, Medicine was a very bloody affair, and as it was also the days before anaesthetics, it was extremely painful and traumatic for patients undergoing any surgical procedure. This put the sensitive Charles Darwin off medicine, so, after two years, he left Edinburgh and joined Cambridge University, where he studied Theology in order to become a country parson. It comes as a shock for some to realize that Darwin's degree was in Theology—and that he did not have any earned scientific qualifications. At Cambridge, however, Darwin was taught a fundamental theological error about Genesis 1; as we shall see, this had a profound effect on how he viewed the Bible as he developed his theory of the origin of species by means of natural selection.

After graduating from Cambridge, Darwin joined HMS *Beagle* as companion to the ship's captain, Robert FitzRoy, and as the resident naturalist. Although Darwin's degree was in Theology, all his life his hobby and interest had been in natural history and he had spent a lot of time at university studying biology and geology. During his voyage on the *Beagle*, and in his subsequent studies after he returned home, Darwin noticed similarities and differences among the plants and animals he observed. For example, the finches on the Galápagos Islands had different bills depending on which island(s) they lived on and therefore on what food they ate. Darwin therefore concluded that all the finches had a common ancestor, and that natural selection caused their beaks to change in order to feed on the food sources that were available on the particular islands on which they lived. This was a problem for him, because in his theological studies at Cambridge, Darwin had been taught (incorrectly) that plants and animals reproduced after their own species and that there was therefore no variation in the offspring. As far as Darwin was concerned, his observations were contrary to the teachings of Genesis 1. But, of course, they weren't!

What Darwin actually observed on the Galápagos Islands was that finches always produce finches. This is *not* contrary to Scripture, but is exactly what Genesis 1 teaches—that plants and animals reproduce after their own *kinds*. It is important to understand the difference between kinds and species. You can get different species within a kind—which is what Darwin observed with the finches on the Galápagos Islands. The different finch species on the Galápagos Islands prove to be only variations within the *finch kind*. Darwin had been taught *incorrectly* that birds, such as finches, reproduce after their own species—but the Bible does not teach this. The Scriptures in Genesis 1 teach the *fixity of kinds* not *the fixity of species*. The English word 'kind' is the correct translation of the Hebrew word *min*. Hence English translations of Genesis 1 show clearly that plants and animals reproduce after their own 'kinds'. In many other European translations of Genesis 1, however, the translators have translated *min* by 'species'. This often causes problems, as it appears from these latter translations that Genesis 1 teaches that plants and animals reproduce after their own *species*. This conclusion is simply the result of a faulty translation and is *not* what the Scriptures teach. This is why it is so important to establish that the Bible we read and study is an accurate translation.

The fact that there are great differences—of varieties as well as species—within a kind can be demonstrated by considering the huge variety that is found within the *wolf–dog kind*. For many years, creationists have used the wolf and the dog, together with all the different breeds of dog that have been bred over the years (at least 350 different breeds have been bred in the last 400 years!), as a perfect example of a biblical kind.[5] I used this example in the first edition of this book as well as in many talks that I have given over the years. Sometimes in my talks, when I have used the wolf–dog kind as a perfect example of the biblical kind, I have been challenged by evolutionists who would not accept it. Today, however, they have to accept it, because in recent years geneticists have confirmed it. They have shown that the domestic dog (including, therefore, all the different breeds) is descended from a single gene pool—that of the wolf: 'The origin of the domestic dog from wolves has been established ... we examined the mitochondrial DNA (mtDNA) sequence variation among 654 domestic dogs representing all major dog populations worldwide ... suggesting a common origin from a single gene pool for all dog populations.'[6] Furthermore, it has also been shown that, not only are dogs and wolves in the same kind, but so also are coyotes and jackals:

Two-kilogram teacup poodles; 90-kg mastiffs; slender greyhounds; squat English bulldogs: For a single species, canines come in a vast array of shapes and sizes. Even more remarkably, they all come from the same stock ... Only subtle differences distinguish dogs from coyotes, jackals, and other canids, making family trees difficult to construct and the timing of the transition from wolf to dog hard to pinpoint.[7]

This is remarkable confirmation of the biblical account of creation—that God made a basic wolf–dog kind and natural and domestic selection has given rise to all the different breeds of dogs as well as such animals as the African wild dog, wolves, coyotes, foxes, jackals and dingoes.

In the plant world, the variation found within a kind can be illustrated by, for example, the different vegetables within the common Wild Mustard species *Brassica oleracea*. Over the years, farmers and horticulturalists have bred at least six different vegetables from this one plant by means of carefully selecting different traits:
- By selecting for stems, you get *kohlrabi*.
- By selecting for lateral buds, you get *Brussels sprouts*.
- By selecting for terminal buds, you get *cabbages*.
- By selecting for flower clusters, you get *cauliflowers*.
- By selecting for stems and flowers, you get *broccoli*.
- By selecting for leaves, you get *kale*.

These varieties of *Brassica*, the different varieties and breeds of dogs within the dog–wolf kind, and the different breeds of horses, pigs, cattle and so on, all demonstrate perfectly the veracity of Genesis 1—that plants and animals reproduce after their own kinds.

These examples of different varieties and breeds are real, are observed, and are the result of *artificial selection*. But different varieties and breeds are also found to be the result of *natural selection*. Although the splitting of the human gene pool occurred at the Tower of Babel, the resulting differing racial characteristics of the human race are the result of natural selection. This is why, for example, we find dark-skinned people living in areas where there is a lot of sunshine, and lighter-skinned people living in areas where there is less sunshine. Natural selection has also resulted in the Inuit, the indigenous people occupying the arctic areas of Canada, Greenland and Alaska, who have a high body fat which insulates them from the cold and also acts as a store of calories to cope with the metabolic heat production induced by the cold. In contrast, natural selection has resulted in the tall, thin people that are found in Central Africa (for example, the Maasai), who are well suited to the hot, dry climate in which they live. These and other examples of natural selection are not examples of evolution. In each case, we see that each kind has within its genome the capacity not only to reproduce, but also to produce great variety; this enables plants, animals and people to populate and enrich the planet.

Natural selection and evolution

In his book about the origin of species, Darwin proposed that *natural selection* was the mechanism for producing, from a single ancestor, all the different species of plants and animals that we find living on the earth today, as well as those found preserved in the fossil record. What, then, is natural selection? It is quite a shock to learn that Darwin did not even define 'natural selection' in his book. After a thorough study of Darwin's book, Harvard-trained lawyer Norman Macbeth argued that Darwin saw natural selection as *differential mortality*—that, for various reasons, among all individuals produced in nature, some die soon and some die late.[8] Natural selection is now thought of as *differential reproduction*, which is associated with reproductive success, or leaving the most offspring. However, as argued by Norman Macbeth, this is tautology:

If we say that evolution is accomplished largely by natural selection and that natural selection consists of differential reproduction, what have we done? Differential reproduction means that some species multiply by leaving more offspring than one-for-one, while others leave one-for-one and remain stable, and others leave less than one-for-one and dwindle or die out. Thus we have as Question: Why do some multiply, while others remain stable, dwindle, or die out? To which is offered as

Answer: Because some multiply, while others remain stable, dwindle, or die out. The two sides of the equation are the same. We have a tautology. The definition is meaningless.[9]

Not only is natural selection meaningless, but it is also invisible—its operations, real or imagined, are not observed by the human eye, as pointed out by Professor George Gaylord Simpson, who was perhaps the most influential palaeontologist of the twentieth century and a major participant in the modern evolutionary synthesis. When discussing a hypothetical case in which animals with trait A survive one time more frequently in 10,000 cases than animals with trait B, he observed, 'By present techniques, it would be quite impossible to observe such weak selection either in the laboratory or in nature ... selection may be highly effective although quite beyond our powers of observation.'[10]

Furthermore, natural selection cannot be quantified—it is impossible to determine the intensity of its action, as pointed out again by Professor Simpson: 'The determination of intensity of selection is in itself a problem to which there is apparently no direct approach and one which it is very difficult to treat practically.'[11]

Natural selection as a mechanism of evolution is therefore fraught with difficulties. It is full of tautology; it is meaningless; it is invisible; and it is non-quantifiable. Yet, in spite of this, biologists still maintain that natural selection is a mechanism of evolution.

Evolutionists believe that what causes any organism to evolve is a change in its genetic make-up. Changes in the gene itself can occur and such changes are called 'mutations'. Mutations do occur in nature and they have been produced in laboratory experiments by the use of high-energy radiation, heat and certain chemicals. However, most mutations are harmful, although some may be advantageous in unusual environments. It is more than likely, however, that a mutation that does cause a change that is considered advantageous in some unusual environment will generally have an injurious physiological effect that will weaken the individual and will therefore be bad.

Mutations, however, are not a mechanism for evolution, as pointed out in the influential biology textbook *Biology: A Search for Order in*

Complexity that was used in many Christian schools and universities in the USA in the 1970s and 1980s:

No one has observed mutations taking place that would change one class of animal into a more complex type of organism: for instance the beginning of a milk gland upon the breast of a reptile, changing it into a mammal; or a feather starting instead of a scale, changing it into a bird. On the other hand, those changes that have been observed are harmful and often involve loss in some physical trait.[12]

We have already seen that careful domestic breeding of plants and animals has achieved some remarkable things. Cross-breeding and selection within a species, such as the common Wild Mustard (*Brassica oleracea*) or a large circle of closely related species, such as wheat, or within a kind, such as the wolf–dog kind or the finch kind, can improve quality and/or diversity. But *Brassica* is still *Brassica*, and not, for example, carrots; wheat is still wheat, and not, for instance, grapefruit; dogs are still dogs and not cats; and finches are still finches and not budgerigars! We can no more grow wings on pigs than we can breed hens that lay cube-shaped eggs!

The full title of Darwin's book is *On the Origin of Species by Means of Natural Selection, or the Preservation of Favoured Races in the Struggle for Life*. We must not forget that Darwin knew nothing of the laws of genetics when he wrote his book. He proposed that natural selection was the cause of evolution. Indeed, it has been maintained by evolutionary biologist Sir Julian Huxley that, 'So far as we now know, not only is Natural Selection inevitable, not only is it an effective agency of evolution, but it is the only effective agency of evolution'.[13]

Factors other than natural selection are involved in causing the enormous variation within a kind (which evolutionists maintain is evolution). These factors include mutations, recombinations of genes and gene flow, fluctuations of population, processes of isolation, as well as processes of selection. Variability, the rate and the character of mutations, the length of generations, and the size of populations also play their part.

The variation in the colour of populations of the peppered moth (*Biston betularia*) is often cited as an example of natural selection and evolution.

The peppered moth exists in two different varieties—a light-coloured variety with dark-coloured splotches and spots; and a dark-coloured variety. To see if natural selection could have caused the colour change in the peppered-moth populations, British ecologist H. B. D. Kettlewell performed an experiment during the late 1950s. He maintained that his experiments showed that the light-coloured moth could hardly be seen when resting on the unpolluted light-grey bark of trees, and so any bird would only be able to see the dark variety. As a result, he maintained that the birds would eat the dark variety and leave the light-coloured one alone. Such selection, he believed, would result in the population of peppered moths being predominantly light-coloured. During the Industrial Revolution, however, soot from industry turned the light-coloured bark of trees nearly black; Kettlewell claimed that the population of the dark-coloured variety then increased—because the dark-coloured variety would be camouflaged and, as a result, birds would only see and therefore eat the light-coloured moths.

This seemed a reasonable explanation, and it was hailed by evolutionists as *the* example of natural selection and of evolution occurring within our lifetime, as stated by Dr Jerry Coyne, Professor of Biology at the University of Chicago: 'Until now, however, the prize horse in our stable of examples [of natural selection] has been the evolution of "industrial melanism" in the peppered moth, *Biston betularia*, presented by most teachers and textbooks as the paradigm of natural selection and evolution occurring within a human lifetime.'[14] However, a thorough review of Kettlewell's work conducted in the late 1990s revealed that the most serious problem with his research is that the peppered moth does not normally rest on tree trunks; precisely two moths were seen in such a position in more than forty years of intensive searches![15] Their natural resting spots are, in fact, a mystery. This alone invalidates Kettlewell's release–recapture experiments. Kettlewell released moths, placing them directly onto tree trunks, where they were highly visible to bird predators. Furthermore, he released his moths during the day, while the moths normally choose resting places at night. Hence Kettlewell's experiments, and consequently his results, are flawed. What is not in doubt, however, is the fact that the peppered moth variations are not the result of evolution.

Interestingly, the peppered moth also lives in North America and exhibits dark forms there despite the absence of any darkening of the trees by industrial pollution. However, it cannot be overstated that the different-coloured moths are still moths of the same species. They are different colours—that is all. This is not evolution—it is a case of variation within the same kind, or, in this case, within the same species. To suggest that such variation can cause fish to evolve into amphibians, then into reptiles and then into mammals is just wishful thinking and is not scientific.

Another mechanism by which evolution is thought to proceed is by 'the survival of the fittest'—a phrase first coined by Herbert Spencer in his 1864 *Principles of Biology*. Darwin first used this phrase in the fifth edition of *On the Origin of Species* published in 1869. This phrase is, however, as meaningless as natural selection: a species survives because it is the fittest, and it is the fittest because it survives. This is circular reasoning—nothing has been explained. It is a metaphor, not a scientific description, and it is misleading.

Having seen the shortcomings of both natural selection and the survival of the fittest as mechanisms for the origin of species, we have to conclude that Darwin was mistaken about the mechanism of the origin of species. As stated above, one of Darwin's other mistakes was to accept what he had been taught at Cambridge about Genesis teaching the fixity of species. His observations demonstrated that there are variations within what he considered to be 'species' (but which are really 'kinds'); as a result, he came to the conclusion that what the Bible taught about the fixity of species was not true. Although it cannot be denied that Charles Darwin was a good observer, what he concluded from his observations—that all plants and animals have descended from a common ancestor—was simply a step too far. Darwin concluded that the small changes he observed (for example, the variation in the size and shape of the beaks of the finches on the Galápagos Islands) add up over eons into big changes that could, for example, change a dinosaur into a bird. This was yet another of his mistakes, demonstrating just how deluded Darwin really was.

Darwin was also deluded about the cause of sin and suffering in the world. He lost the remains of his faith when his ten-year-old daughter Annie died; in a bizarre twist of logic that so many exhibit, he blamed God for all the suffering and death that is in the world and so stopped believing in God! Had he read the Bible, he would have understood that death, disease and suffering came about as the result of Adam's sin. In spite of his loss of faith and professed 'agnosticism', Darwin was buried in Westminster Abbey in London. I personally find it very odd that the established church honoured such a man who was not a Christian and who has caused so many people to become deluded and reject the Scriptures and the God of the Scriptures, as Darwin himself did. Even more bizarre, however, is the fact that in September 2008, the Church of England used its website to issue an apology addressed directly to Darwin some 125 years after his death. The Anglican Church (which originally rejected Darwin's teaching) apologized for misunderstanding his theory, for getting its first reaction wrong, and for having encouraged others to misunderstand his ideas.

Fossils and evolution

Let us now turn our attention to the fossil record—the record of life preserved in the sedimentary rocks on the earth—and see what it teaches about evolution. Dr Duane Gish, former Senior Vice-President at the Institute of Creation Research, first wrote about evolution and the fossil record in 1973 in *Evolution: The Fossils Say No!*, a book which has undergone a number of revisions up to the 1995 completely re-written and updated *Evolution: the Fossils Still Say No!* Dr Henry Morris, writing in the Preface to the 1995 edition, had this to say concerning the fossil record:

The fossil record must provide the critical evidence for or against evolution, since no other scientific evidence can possibly throw light on the actual history of living things ... The time scale of human observation is far too short to permit documentation of real evolutionary change from lower to higher kinds of organisms at the present time. The vital question, therefore, is: 'Does the record of past ages, now preserved in the form of fossils, show that such changes have occurred?'[16]

In this section we will look at the fossil record to see if it shows whether evolution has occurred or not.

In the last chapter we saw that, despite evidence to the contrary, evolutionists maintain that the first living cell evolved from lifeless chemicals, and that this took place over a period of about one billion years some 4,500 to 3,500 million years ago. There is absolutely no fossil evidence that such a cell existed, and there is no fossil evidence for the evolution of the first living cell into multi-cellular organisms, or for the evolution of multi-cellular organisms into invertebrates—that is, animals without backbones. Millions upon millions of fossils representing every major invertebrate life form are found in the fossil record—brachiopods, trilobites, gastropods, sponges, crustaceans, worms, jellyfish, sea urchins, sea cucumbers, sea lilies and so on. These animals are highly complex and their evolution is said to have taken almost 3,000 million years. However, their forerunners are nowhere to be found in the fossil record; not a single fossil of an intermediate that documents the evolution of the invertebrates graces any museum display cabinet, for none exist.

In many cases, many thick (over 1.5 km) sections of sedimentary rock lie in unbroken succession below the strata containing the fossilized remains of these invertebrates, and although the sediments were apparently suitable for the preservation of fossils, because they are often identical with the overlying rocks which are fossiliferous (that is, containing fossils), *no fossils are found in them.* In 1958 Dr Daniel Axelrod, former Professor of Geology and Botany at the University of California, Los Angeles, called this 'one of the major unsolved problems of geology and evolution'.[17] Some thirty-five years later, in 1993, Professor Simon Conway Morris, who at the time of writing is Professor of Evolutionary Palaeobiology in the Department of Earth Sciences at the University of Cambridge, called the emergence of these animals 'the salient mystery in the history of life'.[18] Despite evolutionists' continued searches, the situation has not changed, as noted by Richa Arora in *The Encyclopaedia of Evolutionary Biology* published in March 2004: 'Although there is a good fossil record of the major groups that have well-preserved mineralized skeletons, the origin and evolution of the metazoan phyla cannot be documented from fossil evidence.'[19] The reason why fossils showing the evolution of the invertebrates have not been found is because they simply do not exist!

Commenting on the absence of the ancestors of these creatures, Dr Duane Gish draws the following conclusion:

But creation scientists say, *what greater evidence for creation could the rocks give than this abrupt appearance of a great variety of complex creatures without a trace of ancestors?* Thus we see, right from the beginning, on the basis of an evolutionary scenario, the evidence is directly contradictory to predictions based on evolution but is remarkably in accord with predictions based on creation. *This evidence alone is sufficient to establish the fact that evolution has not occurred on the earth.*[20]

In other words, the invertebrates that we find in the fossil record have no evolutionary history. There are no fossils that are considered to be transitional for any of the major groups of invertebrates that are found in the fossil record. Put simply, there is no fossil evidence that the highly complex and varied invertebrate animals found in the sedimentary rocks evolved from a common ancestor.

The absence of transitional forms is a truth that we encounter over and over again as we consider the origin of the various life forms that we find preserved as fossils in the sedimentary rocks on the earth. According to evolutionists, the invertebrates evolved into vertebrates, that is animals with backbones. Evolutionists believe that the first vertebrates were fish. However, the fossil record does not show any such evolution, as pointed out by anti-creationist Dr Arthur Strahler, emeritus Professor of Geomorphology at the Department of Geology at Columbia University; he admitted that 'the origin of vertebrates is obscure—there is no fossil record preceding the occurrence of fishes'.[21] There are no transitional forms between the invertebrates and fish—vertebrates appear suddenly in the fossil record without any evolutionary history. Furthermore, there is a total absence of ancestors and transitional forms for each major class of fish.

In the same way, there is no fossil evidence for the evolution of fish into amphibians, amphibians into reptiles, and reptiles into mammals. The rock strata have, for example, been searched in vain for a series of fossils showing the evolution of fish into amphibians, but no such series has been found. It used to be argued that the amphibians evolved from the coelacanth fish, which evolutionists believed to have become extinct some eighty million years ago. This idea, however, had to be abandoned in 1938 when some fishermen caught a live specimen of a coelacanth fish off the east coast of South Africa.

In all fish, living or fossil, the pelvic-bones are small and loosely embedded in muscle. In all amphibians, living or fossil, the pelvic-bones are large and firmly attached to the vertebral column. There is not a single transitional form that bridges this basic difference in the anatomy of fish and amphibians. Dr Gish points out that

All the fish cited as being the most likely ancestors of amphibians are 100% fish which were required to spend all of their time in the water, while all of the so-called descendant amphibians were 100% amphibians with the basic amphibian limbs, feet, and legs. No one has succeeded in finding a single transitional form with part fins and part feet.[22]

Not a trace of a transitional intermediate form between fish and amphibians has been found in the fossil record. The only conclusion that can be drawn is that such a transitional form never existed. This is in complete accord with what the Bible teaches: that God created the fish and the amphibians separately—one did not evolve into the other.

Likewise, the evolution of amphibians into reptiles is not substantiated in the fossil record: no transitional forms linking amphibians to reptiles have been found. Reptiles, including flying reptiles, marine reptiles, gliding reptiles, snakes, turtles and dinosaurs, all appear in the fossil record but with no trace of any transitional forms linking them to amphibians.[23] The transitional forms between amphibians and reptiles simply do not exist.

However, the most significant difference between amphibians and reptiles concerns their eggs. Amphibians lay their eggs in water; reptiles lay their eggs in moist-free surroundings, because their eggs are equipped with extra-embryonic membranes. The amniotic egg of a reptile is much more complex than the egg of an amphibian. The egg of a reptile contains a membrane, called the amnion, which provides a sac within which the developing embryo can float. The yolk sac contains a food supply for the developing embryo and the allantois, a membrane in the egg that acts as a reservoir for the waste products that are produced by the developing embryo. The egg is surrounded by a porous shell that allows oxygen to be absorbed into the egg and carbon dioxide to be passed out of the egg. How the simple gelatinous amphibian egg designed for incubation in water could have gradually evolved into the complex amniotic reptile egg designed for incubation in air is a real problem for evolutionists. There is no satisfactory explanation and no fossil evidence for this change.

The evolution of reptiles into mammals is also fraught with problems, as pointed out by Dr Gish:

Another fundamental difference between reptiles and mammals is the fact that all reptiles, living or fossil, have a single bone in the ear, a rod-like bone known as the columella. Mammals possess three bones in the ear, the stapes, malleus, and incus. Evolutionists maintain that the stapes corresponds to the columella and that the quadrate and articular bones of the reptile somehow moved into the ear to become, respectively, the incus and malleus bones of the mammalian ear. No explanation is given how the intermediates managed to hear while this was going on.[24]

Thousands of fossil reptiles have been found, and they all possess a single ear-bone and multiple jaw-bones. Similarly, thousands of fossil mammals have been found that possess three ear-bones and a single jaw-bone. But not a single creature has been found (fossilized or living) representing a reptilian–mammalian transitional form showing, for instance, three jaw-bones or two ear-bones. The idea of bones gradually migrating from the jaw into the ear is also difficult to imagine. Furthermore, how a transitional form would have managed to chew while its jaw was being unhinged and rearticulated is also difficult to imagine. As pointed out by Dr Gish in the above quote, so also is how it managed to hear while its jaw-bones were migrating to its ears!

The absence of transitional forms linking reptiles with the more peculiar kinds of mammals is also very striking. For example, no known transitional forms are known for the marine mammals (whales, dolphins, porpoises, manatees, dugongs, sea cows, sea lions, seals, walruses, turtles and so on), or for the flying mammals (for example, bats), or for the marsupials (for example, kangaroos). In each case, these groups of mammals are found in the fossil record, but no trace of their evolution is found. Their evolutionary origins are represented by missing links and speculations.

Yet, despite the fossil evidence to the contrary, George Gamow and Martynas Ycas gave the following vivid account of the evolution of reptiles into mammals:

The animals changed too. Some of the reptiles in the colder regions began to develop a method of keeping their bodies warm. Their heat output increased when it was cold and their heat loss was cut down when scales became smaller and more pointed, and evolved into fur. Sweating was also an adaptation to regulate the body temperature, a device to cool the body when necessary by evaporation of water. But incidentally the young of these reptiles began to lick the sweat of the mother for nourishment. Certain sweat glands began to secrete a richer and richer secretion, which eventually became milk. Thus the young of these early mammals had a better start in life.[25]

There is absolutely no proof in the fossil record, or anywhere else for that matter, to substantiate such speculations. Such a story is made up of mountains of speculation without a molehill of fact, and is actually the product of the figments of these authors' imaginations. This story about how reptiles changed into mammals is mere fiction—it is not based on scientific fact!

It cannot be overemphasized that, when we look at the fossil record, we find there is no evidence that one kind of plant or animal has changed into another kind of plant or animal. Put simply, in the fossil record we do not find preserved the transitional forms required by Darwin's theory. Darwin himself was actually well aware of this and drew attention to it in *On the Origin of Species* when he wrote, 'Why then is not every geological formation and every stratum full of such intermediate links? Geology assuredly does not reveal any such finely graduated organic chain; and this, perhaps, is the most obvious and gravest objection which can be urged against my theory.'[26] He then suggested that 'The explanation lies, I believe, in the extreme imperfection of the geological record'. Over 150 years since the publication of *On the Origin of Species*, the situation has still not changed, despite the billions of fossils that have been found since then. We do not find the 'graduated organic chain' linking one kind to another. The missing links are still missing!

But there is another problem with the fossil record. Evolutionists maintain that the gradual development of living things occurred so that so-called 'living fossils' should not occur. But they do! And their existence puzzles evolutionists, who must be able to explain why these continue in their old, placid ways without either changing or becoming extinct. In the hundreds of millions of years which the evolutionists allow for evolution to have occurred, 'living fossils' have stubbornly refused to evolve despite changes in climate, environment, enemies, parasites and diseases. Examples of such 'living fossils' are the duck-billed platypus, the little brachiopod called *Lingula*, the opossum, the ginkgo tree, the Australian lungfish and the coelacanth.

We can therefore see from the fossil record that evolution has not been observed in the past. But what about the present? On 3 December 2003, Professor Richard Dawkins was interviewed by Bill Moyers. In the interview, Moyers asked Dawkins, 'Is evolution a theory, not a fact?', to which Dawkins replied, 'Evolution has been observed' and then continued, 'It's just that it hasn't been observed while it's happening.'[27] So evolution has not been observed happening in the past or in the present.

Dinosaurs, birds and evolution

Many people, particularly the young, are fascinated by dinosaurs, perhaps because of their large sizes. When I am invited to speak about these monsters that lived in the past, I have great fun explaining that not all dinosaurs were large, and that one very small dinosaur that has been found was the size of a mouse and is called *Mussaurus*, 'mouse lizard'. However, there is speculation that this small dinosaur was a juvenile and that it could possibly have reached three metres in length and weighed as much as 70 kg when fully grown.[28] It has to be recognized, however, that the average size of a dinosaur was that of a sheep or goat.

It seems reasonable to assume that dinosaurs have become extinct since we do not have them living on the earth today. The question that we therefore need to ask, and to which we need to try to get an answer, is: What happened to the dinosaurs? When my wife and I visited the Natural History Museum in London in March 2007, there was a panel in the section about dinosaurs that stated, 'There are over one hundred published theories about the extinction of the dinosaurs, ranging from the fascinating to the absurd.' Among the more humorous theories put forward is the one to which I was introduced when I was studying Geology as an undergraduate in the mid-1960s—that the dinosaurs died out because the food they ate caused them to be constipated! Some of the more bizarre explanations include their dying out because of sunburn; as a result of being infected with diseases spread by mosquitoes, mites and ticks; or because they were getting the wrong sort of sleep! The most popular (although not necessarily correct) explanation for the fact that dinosaurs are no longer on the earth is that a huge meteor crashed onto the earth and brought the age of the dinosaurs to an abrupt end.

However, some evolutionists maintain that dinosaurs have not become extinct but have evolved into birds. Among them is Dr Mark Norell, Chairman of the Division of Palaeontology and Curator of the 'Dinosaurs: Ancient Fossils, New Discoveries' exhibition at the American Museum of Natural History in New York from 14 May 2005 to 8 January 2006. He is on record stating that 'I would consider that living birds are not only derived from dinosaurs—they are dinosaurs'.[29]

This proposal that birds evolved from dinosaurs and might well be some type of modified dinosaur is simply not substantiated by the fossil record—not a single transitional form linking dinosaurs to birds has been found. The famous fossil bird *Archaeopteryx* is, however, offered as a transitional form by some evolutionists because it possesses some reptilian features. But in fact it is *not* a transitional form. It is a bird—a true bird with wings, feathers identical to those of living flying birds, and a sternum to which the powerful flight muscles were attached.[30] The possession of such features means that *Archaeopteryx* could fly, which means that it was a bird. Although some evolutionists point out that *Archaeopteryx* had reptilian features, so too do some modern living birds (for example, the hoatzin and the *Touraco corythaix*), yet no zoologist considers these two modern birds to be transitional forms.

Furthermore, the feathers of birds are thought to have developed slowly from reptile scales, although this too is unsupported by fossil evidence. Again, no transitional form with part-way feathers has been found in the fossil record, as pointed out by Dr Walter J. Bock, Professor of Evolutionary Biology at Columbia University: '... we lack completely fossils of all intermediate stages between reptilian scales and the most primitive feather.'[31]

There have been reports, however, of fossils of what appear to be dinosaurs with rudimentary or primitive feathers being found in China. Dr Alan Feduccia and his colleagues at the University of North Carolina at Chapel Hill have shown that the fossilized patterns that resemble feathers are in fact bits of decomposed skin and supporting tissues.[32] Feathered dinosaurs have not been found in the fossil record, and any feathers that are seen on dinosaur reconstructions have either been painted on or stuck on with glue!

It cannot be overemphasized that the difference between a scale and a feather is enormous. Scales are flat, horny plates and can be thought of as folds of skin; feathers, on the other hand, are very complex in structure and consist of a central shaft, the rachis, from which radiate barbs and, from them, barbules. The anterior barbules have tiny hooks at their ends and these lock onto the ends of the posterior barbules, resulting in the formation of a flat, strong, flexible vane. The differences continue. Scales and feathers arise from different layers of skin: feathers develop from follicles and are protected by a horny sheath and form around a bloody, conical, inductive dermal core.

One of the problems that evolutionists have about such transformations concerns genetics. Where does the *new* genetic information come from in order to change a dinosaur's scale into the complex feather of a bird? Where does the new genetic information come from in order to create something so delicate and yet so strong as a flight feather? Where does the new genetic information come from in order to create the rachis of a feather with its two veins, which are composed of hundreds of barbs? Where does the new genetic information come from to create the hundreds of barbules that are found on each barb? Where does the new genetic information come from in order to create the hooks that are found on the anterior barbules and which hook over the posterior barbules to enable the whole feather to be 'zipped up' and form something so incredibly light and strong? It is difficult to imagine the origin of the new genetic information required to cause such a transformation and, as we have seen, there is no evidence for such a transformation in the fossil record. Any explanation that evolutionists give regarding such a transformation should be regarded as being what Dr Gish calls 'nothing more than empty rhetoric without a shred of empirical content'.33 Yet, when those who believe Genesis suggest that feathers have been designed by Almighty God, this is ridiculed and is not considered to be a valid hypothesis. The reason for this has been explained by the immunologist Professor Scott Todd of Kansas State University in a letter to *Nature*: 'Even if all the data point to an intelligent designer, such an hypothesis is excluded from science because it is not naturalistic.'34

This helps to explain why there can be no dialogue between creationists and evolutionists. The evolutionists require a natural explanation for everything and will not permit any supernatural explanation when it comes to discussing origins.

But let us return to the demise of the dinosaurs. There appears to be evidence that dinosaurs did not become extinct a long time ago, but that they were around in more recent times.

The *first* piece of evidence is found in the Bible. In the book of Job, which dates back to the second millennium BC, there is mention of the huge animal 'behemoth' in Job 40 (v. 15). 'Behemoth' is simply a transliteration of the Hebrew word used there. Although this animal is not given any other name, its description implies that it is the largest and most powerful animal ever to have existed. One interesting feature of this animal is that, according to Job 40:17, it has a tail like a cedar tree. The only animal that matches such a description is a sauropod dinosaur, such as a brachiosaur, and all the other features of behemoth described in Job 40 confirms this. This could therefore indicate that brachiosaur dinosaurs were alive in Job's day, that is, less than 4,000 years ago.

The *second* piece of evidence comes from rock-carvings (petroglyphs) found at the Natural Bridges National Monument in the south-east corner of the state of Utah, USA.35 These petroglyphs, which were made by the Anasazi Indians 500 to 1,500 years ago, show various animals, humans and even hand-prints. Some of these stone carvings depict creatures that are indisputable brachiosaur dinosaurs. This means that dinosaurs were living in south-east Utah between 500 and 1,500 years ago.

The *third* piece of evidence that dinosaurs were living recently is found at the temple at Angkor Wat in Cambodia.[36] Here, there is a stone carving of what is indisputably a stegosaurus dinosaur, showing clearly the upright plates on its back that are characteristic of this dinosaur. No other animals had these plates on their backs, and this carving, which dates from the early twelfth century, clearly shows these plates. This therefore presents clear evidence that the stegosaurus dinosaur was living in Cambodia about 900 years ago.

The *fourth* piece of evidence that dinosaurs were living recently comes from a tomb found in Carlisle Cathedral in north-west England.[37] In the floor of the cathedral, in the gangway between the choir stalls, lies the tombstone of Bishop Richard Bell, who lived from 1410 to 1496. The tomb is almost three metres long and has an inlaid brass carving of the bishop in a gothic canopy, dressed in his full vestments, wearing a mitre (his bishop's hat) and holding a crosier (the hooked staff of a bishop). Around the edge of the tomb is an inlaid brass fillet with carvings of different animals—various fish, an eel, a dog, a pig, a bird and a weasel/stoat. Among the animals is one creature that looks totally out of place—an animal that looks for all the world like a brachiosaurus dinosaur! The most remarkable thing about these carvings is the accurate portrayal of their limbs. When dinosaur fossils were first discovered, it was thought that the animals from which they were descended were reptilian; when they were reconstructed they were therefore shown with their limbs sticking out from the sides of their bodies, like crocodiles or lizards. It was only when some dinosaurs were found fossilized in mud that it was realized that their limbs came from beneath their bodies. And this is how the dinosaurs on Bishop Bell's tomb are depicted—with their legs on the underside of their bodies. Here is further evidence that the sauropod dinosaurs lived, this time in England, at the end of the fifteenth century.

The *fifth* and final piece of evidence that dinosaurs were living recently comes mainly from the discoveries made by Dr Mary Schweitzer, a palaeontologist at the North Carolina State University. Since the early 1990s, she has found soft-tissue cell-like microstructures, flexible and fibrous bone material, transparent and pliable blood vessels and red blood cells in a *Tyrannosaurus rex* bone dug out of sandstone from the fossil-rich Hell Creek Formation in Montana, USA. Her findings were published by the prestigious Royal Society in January 2007.[38] Since then, she and her colleagues have recovered protein fragments from the fossilized remains of the duck-billed dinosaur, *Brachylophosaurus canadensis*.[39] These finds alone confirm that the dinosaurs lived recently, as it is impossible for proteins, blood cells and other cellular structures to survive without being degraded or fossilized for the sixty-five-plus million years demanded by evolutionists.

Evolutionists ignore the evidence given above that dinosaurs lived recently. Instead, they cling on to the idea that dinosaurs lived millions of years ago and that they evolved into birds, even though, as we have seen, there is no evidence for this supposed evolution.

Conclusion

At the beginning of this chapter, we reviewed briefly the life and beliefs of Charles Darwin and saw that he was deluded, especially about what the Bible teaches about the origin of species within kinds. We saw that, in actual fact, his observations of the finches on the Galápagos Islands confirmed the Genesis account of creation—that plants and animals reproduce after their own kinds. Having seen the shortcomings of both natural selection and the survival of the fittest as mechanisms for the origin of all the different plants and animals that we find on the earth today and also in the fossil record, we have to conclude that Darwin was mistaken about the mechanism of the origin of species.

Having looked carefully at the fossil record, we have to conclude with Dr Duane Gish that the fossils continue to shout a resounding 'No!' to evolution. We have seen that the supposed evolution of dinosaurs into birds is not confirmed by the fossil record, and that there is overwhelming evidence—from a written description, drawings, carvings and the remains of soft tissues, including red blood cells—to suggest that dinosaurs were living on the earth recently.

Despite all the evidence against evolution having taken place in the past, or taking place in the present, people are still inclined to believe in evolution for one reason or another. When they cannot provide any evidence, they indulge in wishful thinking, as Charles Darwin did in *On the Origin of Species*. In the first edition, he wrote that 'I can see no difficulty in

Chapter 8

a race of bears being rendered, by natural selection, more and more aquatic in their structure and habits, with larger and larger mouths, till a creature was produced as monstrous as a whale'.[40] The reason why Charles Darwin could write such nonsense was because he was ignorant of genetics that show genetic homeostasis—that all attempts to transform one kind of plant or animal into another demonstrate that there are strict genetic barriers that will not allow such a transformation. In other words, there are genetic barriers to each kind, preventing one kind being changed into another, different kind. This shows the reliability of the clear teaching of the Word of God in Genesis 1, where we read about plants and animals reproducing after their own kinds.

Notes

1 See 'History of Evolutionary Thought', at: en.wikipedia.org.
2 **H. M. Morris,** *The Troubled Waters of Evolution* (San Diego: Creation-Life, 1974), p. 55.
3 **Ernst Mayr,** *Animal Species and Evolution* (Cambridge, MA: Belknap Press of Harvard University Press, 1963), p. 12.
4 **G. Simpson,** *This View of Life* (New York: Harcourt, Brace & World, 1964), p. 81.
5 See **Henry M. Morris** and **John C. Whitcomb,** *The Genesis Flood* (London: Evangelical Press, 1969), p. 66.
6 **Savolainen et al.,** 'Genetic Evidence for an East Asian Origin of Domestic Dogs', in *Science*, 298/5598 (2002), pp. 1610–1613.
7 **Elizabeth Pennisi,** 'Canine Evolution: A Shaggy Dog History', in *Science*, 298/5598 (2002), pp. 1540–1542.
8 **Norman Macbeth,** *Darwin Retried* (New York: Dell, 1971), p. 40.
9 Ibid. p. 47.
10 **G. G. Simpson,** *The Major Features of Evolution* (New York: Simon & Schuster, 1967), p. 146.
11 **G. G. Simpson,** *Tempo and Mode in Evolution* (New York: Columbia University Press, 1944), p. 81.
12 **J. H. Moore** and **H. S. Slusher,** *Biology: A Search for Order in Complexity* (Grand Rapids, MI: Zondervan, 1974), p. 98.
13 **Julian Huxley,** *Evolution in Action* (New York: Mentor, 1957), p. 35.
14 **Professor Jerry Coyne,** 'Not Black and White', review of **Michael Majerus,** *Melanism:*

Evolution in Action (Oxford: Oxford University Press, 1998), in *Nature*, vol. 396 (5 November 1998), p. 36.

15 Ibid.

16 Henry Morris, 'Preface', in **Duane T. Gish,** *Evolution: The Fossils Still Say No!* (San Diego: Institute for Creation Research, 1995), p. v.

17 Daniel Axelrod, 'Early Cambrian Marine Fauna', in *Science*, vol. 128 (4 July 1958), p. 7.

18 S. C. Morris, quoted in **Gish,** *Evolution: The Fossils Still Say No!*, p. 61.

19 Richa Arora, *Encyclopaedia of Evolutionary Biology* ([n.p.]: Anmol Publications Pvt, 2004), p. 226.

20 Gish, *Evolution: The Fossils Still Say No!*, p. 69.

21 Arthur N. Strahler, *Science and Earth History: The Evolution/Creation Controversy* (Buffalo, NY: Prometheus, 1987), p. 316.

22 Gish, *Evolution: The Fossils Still Say No!*, p. 92.

23 The complete lack of transitional forms between amphibians and the different forms of reptiles is documented in **Gish,** *Evolution: The Fossils Still Say No!*, pp. 97–129.

24 Gish, *Evolution: The Fossils Still Say No!*, p. 167.

25 George Gammov and **Martynas Ycas,** *Mr Tomkins Inside Himself* (London: Allen & Unwin, 1968), p. 149.

26 Charles Darwin, *On the Origin of Species* (London: Penguin, 1968), p. 292.

27 *NOW* with **Bill Moyers,** 3 December 2004, PBS; transcript at: pbs.org.

28 See 'Mussaurus' on Wikipedia, at: en.wikipedia.org.

29 Quoted in **Joe Cellini,** 'Tyrannosaurus Wren?', at: apple.com/pro/video/naturalhistory.

30 The finding of the seventh specimen of *Archaeopteryx* was reported in 1993 and it included a bony sternum. No evidence of a bony sternum had been found on the previous six specimens, which had led evolutionists to conclude that *Archaeopteryx* either could not fly or was a poor flier.

31 W. J. Bock, 'Explanatory Theory of the Origin of Feathers', in *American Zoology*, vol. 40 (2000), p. 480.

32 'Scientists Say No Evidence Exists that Therapod Dinosaurs Evolved into Birds', in *Science Daily*, 10 October 2005; at: sciencedaily.com/releases/2005/10/051010085411.htm.

33 Gish, *Evolution: The Fossils Still Say No!*, p. 137.

34 Correspondence, *Nature*, 410/6752 (30 September 1999), p. 423.

35 Doug Sharp, 'Dinosaur Petroglyphs at Natural Bridges National Monument', 7 June 2001, at: rae.org/dinoglyph.html.

36 'Dinosaurs in Ancient Cambodian Temple', at: bible.ca/tracks/tracks-cambodia.htm.

37 Philip Bell, 'Bishop Bell's Brass Behemoths', in *Creation*, 25/4 (September 2003), pp. 40–44; also at: creation.com.

38 Mary Higby Schweitzer, Jennifer L. Wittmeyer and **John R. Horner,** 'Soft Tissue and Cellular Preservation in Vertebrate Skeletal Elements from the Cretaceous to the Present', in *Proceedings of the Royal Society*, B22, 274/1607 (January 2007), pp. 183–197.

39 Mary H. Schweitzer et al., 'Biomolecular Characterization and Protein Sequences of the Campanian Hadrosaur *B. canadensis*', 1 May 2009, at: sciencemag.org. This was also reported in *Chemistry World* (June 2009), p. 4.

40 Charles Darwin, *On the Origin of Species: A Facsimile of the First Edition* (Cambridge, MA: Harvard University Press, 1964), p. 184.

The origin of humans

From November 2008 to April 2009, the Darwin Big Idea Big Exhibition was held at the Natural History Museum in London. In this exhibition it was stated that 'all modern humans are descendants of people who lived in Africa between 100,000 and 150,000 years ago'.[1] In spite of this bold assertion, however, it would appear that, at present, evolutionists are reluctant to commit themselves to giving us a detailed account of this evolution, with exact descriptions of each stage of this evolution of ape-like creatures into humankind.[2] Perhaps the reason for this is the mistakes and blunders that evolutionists have made over the last one-and-a-half centuries; they are perhaps deliberately vague about the process of this supposed evolution so that they will not be easily made to look fools in the future.

The reason why evolutionists now believe that humans evolved from apes in Africa is because this is what Charles Darwin advocated in 1871. He argued that, because the closest living relatives of modern humans (that is, the chimpanzee and the gorilla) are both confined to Africa, it is probable that the common ancestor of modern humans also lived in Africa. This argument is, of course, based on the premise that chimpanzees and gorillas are our closest living relatives. Why do evolutionists believe this? It is because chimpanzees and gorillas have a similar anatomical structure to that of humans, and because their biochemistry (for example, the chemicals that make up their proteins) is also similar.

The argument is based on the *assumption* that, because these three creatures (humans, chimpanzees and gorillas) are similar, they therefore have a common ancestor. But this has not been proven! It is like arguing that, because different cars have a similar shape and similar components, they have therefore evolved from a common ancestral car! In fact, the reason why cars are similar is because they have been designed and modified (for use as family cars, sports cars, vans, etc.) and have been constructed from similar components (engines, gear boxes, batteries, electrical components, seats, etc.). This 'design argument' is also the reason why humans, chimpanzees and gorillas have similar body shapes and biochemistry: because they have been created by the same Designer—Almighty God. Their similarity has nothing to do with evolution from a common ancestor.

Past mistakes and frauds

Despite Darwin suggesting an 'out of Africa' ancestry for humans, in the middle of the nineteenth century and in the early part of the twentieth century evolutionists had other ideas. They were insisting that the evolution of humans from their ape-like ancestors took place in Central Europe, England or in the USA. This was simply because the European nations and the USA were considered to have advanced civilizations. This resulted not only in claims that some very odd ape-people—the Neanderthals, Piltdown Man and Nebraska Man—had been 'discovered', but also in a number of mistakes being made and even fraud being perpetrated in the name of science.

First of all, let us look at how and why the earliest depictions of the Neanderthals were ape-like in their appearance. The Neanderthals are named after the German Neander Valley[3] (*Neandertal* in German), where the first fossilized remains of a Neanderthal were discovered in August 1856. Some quarrymen were clearing out a cave, the entrance of which was over eighteen metres up a precipitous cliff. Among the debris from the cave floor they found some bones which they brought to the attention of Dr Johann Carl Fuhlrott, a local teacher and amateur naturalist. He took them to Professor Hermann Schaaffhausen, who was Professor of Anatomy at the University of Bonn. Professor Schaaffhausen is credited as naming Neanderthal Man and presenting him to the world in 1857.

When they were first discovered, it was thought that the Neanderthals were *the* link between apes and humans. Consequently, Neanderthals were depicted as having divergent toes, just like the apes, and as walking on the outer edges of their feet, just like orang-utans. It was said that the Neanderthals could not straighten their knees and that they lacked the convex spine for upright posture. Their heads, with their heavy eyebrow ridges, retreating foreheads and protruding jaws, were depicted as jutting forward, just like those of gorillas. Their faces were given large eye-sockets, broad noses and receding chins. All this was done to emphasize the ape-like appearance of these creatures because it was firmly believed that the Neanderthals were half-ape/half-human.

Since the discovery of the first Neanderthal in the middle of the nineteenth century, many hundreds of specimens of Neanderthal have been found all over Europe (Belgium, the Channel Islands, Croatia, England, France, Germany, Gibraltar, Greece, Italy and Spain), the Middle East (Iraq, Israel, Syria and Uzbekistan) and North Africa (Morocco). A Neanderthal jaw-bone has even been dredged up from the seabed of the North Sea.[4] Research on these discoveries has established that the curve of the limb-bones of some of the skeletons was due to rickets, a disease caused by vitamin-D deficiency. Other research has shown that the stooped skeletal structure of other Neanderthals (especially the one found at La Chapelle-aux-Saints in central France in 1908) was the result of those individuals suffering from arthritis, and had nothing at all to do with their being in any way ape-like.

There is still much debate about the relationship between the Neanderthals and modern humans. Some anthropologists maintain that the Neanderthals are a sub-species of *Homo sapiens* and think that they should be designated *Homo sapiens neanderthalensis*. This would mean that modern humans are also a sub-species of *Homo sapiens* and would have to be designated *Homo sapiens sapiens*. Others argue that the Neanderthals' DNA places them outside the reaches of the variation that we find in modern humans (*Homo sapiens*) and so they should be classified as a different species altogether—*Homo neanderthalensis*. This is surprising as there is evidence that modern humans and Neanderthals interbred.[5] More analysis of the Neanderthal genome is expected to throw further light on this.[6]

Remains of Neanderthals that have been found also indicate that they commonly hunted large animals, including horses and mammoths; that they used fire and hotplates to cook their food; that they were proficient at crafting basic tools and weapons; that they fashioned flutes from bone; that they attempted writing; and that they buried their dead in graves, some of which contained flowers that are known to have medicinal properties, indicating that they had a rudimentary knowledge of medicine. All this evidence seems to suggest that the Neanderthals were indeed human; from what the Bible teaches about the creation and early history of the earth, this should not surprise us.

The idea that Neanderthals were human is supported by what a couple of anatomists wrote about them as long ago as 1957.[7] They concluded that there was 'no valid reason for assuming that the posture of Neanderthal Man differed significantly from that of present day man', and they went on to say that if a Neanderthal male was bathed, shaved and dressed in modern clothing, he would pass unnoticed on the New York subway. The humanness of the Neanderthals is further demonstrated by the fact that, when the faces of Neanderthals are recreated using forensic science techniques that involve computer morphing, the results show that the Neanderthals looked human. Furthermore, Dr Svante Paabo of the Max Planck Institute for Evolutionary Anthropology in Leipzig, Germany, stated in 2007 that 'If you saw one [a Neanderthal] she or he would strike you as very robust and muscular with a big brow ridge and bigger musculature [the muscular system of the body]. But they had, for example, just as big a brain as we have.'[8]

We have to accept, therefore, that the early reconstructions of Neanderthals were incorrect, mistakes having been made as a result of misdiagnoses of illnesses—rickets and arthritis, to be precise. Our concept of Neanderthals must therefore change. Instead of thinking of them as being shambling, frowning brutes of low intelligence, we should think of them as our cousins. They used animal skins for clothing and even sewed them together. We have to accept that they lived in caves—but so did some people in England until the 1960s,[9] and even today many people still live in caves in many countries. The Neanderthals actually built shelters of saplings covered with animal skins and furs within the mouths of the caves. We can therefore imagine these red-headed[10] Neanderthal cousins of ours sitting in their shelters within their caves at night, eating their mammoth stew which has been cooked over the fire, or eating their mammoth steaks which they have cooked on their hotplates. Meanwhile, some of their friends and relatives entertain themselves by playing music on their flutes, while others sing along or dance by the light of the fire.

Now let us look, not at another mistake, but at a fraud. We have seen that it took over a hundred years for evolutionists to realize that they had made mistakes in the reconstructions of Neanderthal people. It took them over forty years to realize that the Piltdown Man was a fraud: that what was considered to be the remains of a half-ape/half-human creature was in fact the remains of a woman and an orang-utan.

The story of the discovery of Piltdown Man starts at the beginning of the twentieth century, when some labourers found a few pieces of old bones while digging in a gravel pit near the village of Piltdown in East Sussex, south-east England. Realizing the potential value of these bones, their employer gave them to Charles Dawson, a local archaeologist, and it was he who verified their antiquity and pronounced them to be parts of a skull that was possibly human. Dawson began to search for the rest of the skull and in 1912 a jaw-bone was uncovered. Arthur Woodward of the British Museum verified that the bones were ancient, that the skull had human features and that the jaw was ape-like. Whether the jaw fitted the skull could not be determined because the point of attachment, or joint, on the jaw was missing. The fossils became known as Piltdown Man and were given the scientific name *Eoanthropus dawsoni*, which means 'Dawson's dawn-man'.

In 1915, more fossils were found in a gravel pit adjacent to the site of the original find. Other fossils—a canine tooth and a tool made from a fossil elephant thigh-bone—had been uncovered in the same stratum and these finds supported the conclusions reached from the first find. Piltdown Man therefore appeared to be a creature that had both ape-like and human-like characteristics, and reconstructions of him were put on prominent display in museums all over the world. Here, they declared, was incontrovertible proof that humans had evolved from apes, and that they did so in England!

What was not known at the time was that Piltdown Man was a fraud, one that stayed undetected for over forty years. It was not until 1953 that the cranium was shown to be human and the jaw-bone was shown to be from an orang-utan. It was shown that both the cranium and the jaw had been stained to make them appear old, and that the teeth in the jaw had been filed in order to make them look more human. It was also shown that the bones in the original site, together with the materials in the adjacent site, had been deliberately planted in these areas.

The identity of the person responsible for this forgery will never be known because it happened a hundred years ago and all the people concerned with the discovery of Piltdown Man are now dead. It is worth noting, however, that politicians in the UK were so shocked when the forgery was uncovered, and by the fact that it had gone undetected for so long, that a motion was tabled in the House of Commons 'that the House has no confidence in the Trustees of the British Museum'.[11]

But it was not only in the UK that people were eager to accept that humans had evolved from apes in their own country; it also happened in the USA. The Piltdown Man was a fraud, but in the USA, Nebraska Man turned out to be an appalling mistake. In March 1922, Harold Cook, an amateur geologist, sent a fossil tooth that he had found in 1917 to Henry Fairfield Osborn, who at the time was not only President of the New York Zoological Society, but also President of the American Museum of Natural History. Cook informed Osborn that he had found this fossil tooth in the Snake Creek fossil beds in the Pliocene (now designated Miocene) deposits in the state of Nebraska and, thinking that it might be from some kind of ape-man, he had decided to send it to him. Osborn believed that he could see that the tooth had human, chimpanzee and ape-man characteristics and declared that the tooth spoke volumes of truth and afforded evidence of humankind's descent from apes. Osborn gave the scientific name *Hesperopithecus haroldcookii* ('Harold Cook's ape from the land where the sun sets') to the creature from which the tooth had come.

Osborn's views were fully supported and promoted by eminent anatomist and anthropologist Professor Sir Grafton Elliot Smith, who was Professor of Anatomy at University College, London. A drawing of Nebraska Man by the artist Amedee Forestier subsequently appeared in the *Illustrated London News* on 24 June 1922. This illustration showed a club-wielding half-ape/half-human Nebraska Man with his wife crouching by his side in exotic prehistoric surroundings, complete with primitive horses and camels nearby. It is truly amazing how a single tooth can give such inspiration to an artist!

In spring 1925, however, a team from the American Museum of Natural History went to the site where Harold Cook had found the fossil tooth and there they found other fossilized remains. They were then able to establish that the creature from which the original tooth had come was an extinct peccary—a kind of pig. The news made the front page of the *New York Times* and the story was picked up by *The Times* in London. In 1927, the idea that Nebraska Man was a half-ape/half-human creature was retracted in an article in *Science*, leaving evolutionists with no evidence for the existence of half-ape/half-human creatures in the USA.[12]

Mistakes that were made in the Neanderthal reconstructions and the claims for Nebraska Man, together with the Piltdown Fraud, should make us wary of accepting any drawing or model as a true representation of what so-called ape-people looked like. We have seen that such reconstructions are no more than figments of the imaginations of the artists who drew or reconstructed them. You might think that it was because of ignorance that errors were made in the middle of the nineteenth and twentieth centuries, and that such errors would not be repeated in our more sophisticated age. But you would be very wrong. We will now look at a fraud and a number of mistakes that were made towards the end of the twentieth century and even at the beginning of this century.

Recent mistakes and frauds

In 1971, the National Geographic Society reported the discovery of the Tasaday Tribe, a tribe of people living in caves deep in the rainforest on the remote island of Mindanao, 600 miles south-east of Manila in the Philippines.[13] Naked members of this tribe using stone tools were photographed by a *National Geographic* photographer and, as a result, it was believed that here was a Stone Age tribe living in the Space Age! In 1987, a film crew from British Central Television paid a return visit to the Tasaday Tribe and the result was broadcast the following year.[14] This broadcast showed men and women who were easily recognized from the original media coverage living in ordinary huts, raising normal crops, and wearing tatty T-shirts and frayed jeans. This was not because they had been exposed too often to Western civilization or because members of the TV crew had given them some 'trendy clothing', but rather because they had taken part in a hoax! They had never lived in caves, but every time visitors came, they left their huts, took off their clothes and played elaborate charades in the caves. Their Stone Age tools turned out to be pebbles that they had picked out of the stream. They had done all this for money that had been promised them by government officials—but the money never materialized. The anthropologists who originally studied these people had only seen what their preconceived evolutionary ideas had wanted them to see.

In the 1980s there were a couple of examples of evolutionists being deceived by their own preconceived ideas. One concerned the mistaken identification of a dolphin's rib that was thought to be the collar-bone of some half-ape/half-human creature.[15] The other was a skull fragment that had been found in the Andalusia region of Spain. This skull fragment was heralded as being from the oldest example of a human in Eurasia and was given the name 'Orce Man' after the name of the town near to where it had been found. The skull was subsequently shown to be from a four-month-old donkey![16]

In the 1990s, mistakes were still being made. Towards the end of September 1994, newspaper and TV news headlines declared that *the* missing link between apes and humans had been discovered. These headlines were based on a paper published in the prestigious journal *Nature* by Professor Tim White of the University of California, Berkeley.[17] The paper reported that the fossilized remains of this creature had been found by White and his colleagues in the region known as Middle Awash, which lies each side of the Awash River in the Afar Depression in Ethiopia. When the fossilized remains were looked at carefully, however, it was shown that they came from seventeen individuals. In the cases of thirteen, all that had been found was some teeth. Another individual was represented by a piece of a lower jaw, and another by the base of a skull. In the other two cases, one individual was represented by a right humerus, and the other by a left humerus, radius and ulna. Apart from a piece of a lower jaw, a fragment of a cranium and four arm-bones, no other bones were found—no vertebrae, no ribs, no shoulder blades, no hips, no legs, no feet-bones and no hand-bones. On the basis of what had been found, it was impossible to determine whether this creature walked upright, like a human, or on its four limbs, like a chimpanzee. However, *Australopithecus ramidus*, as the creature was called, was heralded as the immediate descendant of the common ancestor of humans and chimpanzees.

A year later, however, *Australopithecus ramidus* was quietly assigned to a new genus and given the name *Ardipithecus ramidus*.[18] This creature is now thought to be the ancestor of the australopithecines, which are extinct apes. This announcement was not heralded by any of the news media. This means that what is in people's minds is that, in 1994, *the* ape–human link was found, whereas evolutionists are now saying that an ape–ape link was found! No wonder people are confused about what has been found when the news media propagate the discovery of what is supposed to be *the* ape–human link but then fail to mention when this creature is shown *not* to be such a link. What is left in people's minds is that the evolutionists have proved over and over again that humans have evolved from ape-like ancestors, when in fact this is manifestly untrue.

But mistakes continue to be made—even in the twenty-first century. As we shall see in the next section, the most famous australopithecine that has been found was discovered in 1974 and was given the name 'Lucy'. In 2006, the fossil remains of a juvenile australopithecine were found in Ethiopia, and this juvenile has been called 'Lucy's Baby', although she is not the daughter of Lucy and the evidence suggests that she probably lived *before* Lucy did. When the discovery of Lucy's Baby was first reported, however, once again the mainstream media served up their usual hype and propaganda in support of the evolutionary theory of the origin of humans. For example, writing about this find in the *National Geographic News* on 20 September 2006, staff writer James Owen declared that the skeleton belonged to the 'primitive human species *Australopithecus afarensis*'.[19] We will look at the different species within the australopithecines in the next section, but to say that the australopithecines were human is a complete distortion of the truth, for the australopithecines are nothing more than extinct apes.

It is interesting to find out exactly what the anthropologists had found. The original paper published in *Nature* about 'Lucy's Baby' stated that the fossil bones had been collected by six different people over a period of three years[20]—something not mentioned on the BBC website, which gave the impression that an almost-complete skeleton had been found together in one place: 'The find consists of the whole skull, the entire torso and important parts of the upper and lower limbs. CT scans reveal unerupted teeth still in the jaw, a detail that makes scientists think the individual may have been about three years old when she died.'[21]

We can rightly conclude, however, that the skull did in fact come from a juvenile australopithecine. This was confirmed by a study of the semicircular canals that showed that they are ape-like in orientation—that is, they are not adapted for upright walking. This shows that the skull came from a creature that was more like a chimpanzee than a human. Furthermore, the bones of the only complete finger of Lucy's Baby are curved like those of a chimpanzee, and this further strengthens the argument that this creature was ape-like from the waist up and appears to be more akin to a chimpanzee than to a human. Unfortunately, not a great deal can be deduced from the pelvis or lower extremities, as much of them is missing.

After extensive consideration of all the findings of Lucy's Baby, anatomist Dr Brad Harrub has concluded,

The media proved once again that they are less concerned with the truth than with eagerly supporting the humanistic and atheistic views espoused by Neo-Darwinians. An unbiased analysis of the anatomy of this creature clearly demonstrates that greater care should be given when reporting to the public. To assign this creature as a 'missing link' or 'Lucy's Baby' is misleading, when the evidence points more towards this creature being simply an ape (probably chimpanzee) ... The semicircular canals demonstrate this creature was not a biped, and the remaining anatomical findings argue strongly that the latest 'missing link' is still missing.[22]

The reconstruction of this 'precious little bundle', as George Washington University anthropologist Bernard Wood called her,[23] seemed to have been yet another case of mistaken identity.

The final case of mistaken identity we will look at here is a very recent one. In 1995, Dr Russell Ciochon, Professor of Anthropology at the University of Iowa, together with his colleagues, found in the Longgupo cave in Sichuan Province, China, a fragment of a fossilized jaw with two teeth attached to it. They believed that this fossil belonged to an early human ancestor. At the time it was considered to be the oldest human fossil in Asia. Later finds have, however, shown that Professor Ciochon's conclusion—that this fossil jaw and teeth were from a human—was wrong. To his credit, Professor Ciochon has now changed his mind and has reclassified it as an ape fossil. Professor Ciochon has been very public about his change of mind and wrote an essay which was published in *Nature* in June 2009.[24]

As we have seen, it sometimes takes dozens of years before a fraud or mistake is exposed, and this is only accepted if the exposure is done by an evolutionist. Any questions that are raised by creationists about the authenticity or interpretation of any fossil are immediately dismissed by evolutionists. Who knows what interpretations of fossil remains that are currently accepted as bona fide will be exposed as fraudulent or just simply mistaken in the next twenty or so years? Who knows whether what we now accept as a perfect reconstruction of a creature will be found to be seriously in error as more fossils are found in the future?

This is something we need to bear in mind whenever there is a news item about the finding of yet another missing link. We must not be perplexed by such claims. In time, most likely the claims will be declared as just more mistakes, or as misidentified apes or misidentified humans. In my opinion, a sceptical approach to the findings and reconstructions of so-called half-ape/half-human creatures does not go amiss.

Australopithecines—fossil apes

What anthropologists believe about the evolution of humans is based on their preconceived ideas. As we have already seen, Charles Darwin, for example, believed that humans evolved from ape-like ancestors in Africa. We have seen that he argued that the closest living relatives of modern humans—the chimpanzee and the gorilla—were both confined to Africa, and so it was probable that the common ancestor of modern humans was also likely to have lived in Africa. Such a conclusion was based on the premise that chimpanzees and gorillas are our closest living relatives. What is the evidence, if any, for this? We have seen that the evidence is simply an assumption: it is assumed that, because humans, chimpanzees and gorillas have similar body parts, they have a common ancestry. This assumption should be recognized as such. It is interesting to look at what has happened in the evolutionists' quest for the origin of humans because of this and similar assumptions.

In the later part of the nineteenth century, the famous German naturalist and evolutionist Professor Ernst Haeckel was so convinced that ape-people existed that he commissioned a drawing of such a creature, even though there was *no* tangible evidence that such a creature had ever existed. He even named this hypothetical creature *Pithecanthropus alanthus*, which means 'ape-man without speech'. Haeckel believed that, because our nearest living relative is the orang-utan, humans must have evolved from their ape-like ancestors in South-East Asia, where orang-utans are found. Indoctrinated by the preconceived ideas of Haeckel, who was his former professor, a young Dutch doctor, Eugène Dubois, went to the Far East in 1887, determined to find this hypothetical half-ape/half-human creature.

Eventually Dubois was convinced that he had found what he was looking for at Trinil on the island of Java. There he found a couple of molar teeth, the broken cap of a skull, a human leg-bone and several leg-bone fragments. Dubois named his find *Pithecanthropus erectus* ('upright ape-man') and Professor Haeckel commissioned the construction of a life-size model of this upright ape-man so that 'Java Man' (as he was commonly called) could be exhibited in museums throughout Europe. What Dubois had not told anyone is that he had found the bones and teeth in separate places and there was no reason to believe that they had come from the same individual. The only reason why he believed that they had come from the same individual was because he was convinced that he would find a half-ape/half-human creature in the Far East and he made sure that he appeared to have done so, irrespective of what he had actually found.

We saw above that mistakes have been unintentionally made when fossil bones and teeth have been used to reconstruct the individual from whom the bones and teeth have come. We would do well, however, to remember G. K. Chesterton's words when we look at such reconstructions. Writing about Java Man (remember that Java Man was reconstructed from just a couple of molar teeth, the broken cap of a skull, a human leg-bone and several leg-bone fragments), Chesterton wrote,

People talked of *Pithecanthropus* as of Pitt or Fox or Napoleon. Popular histories published portraits of him like the portraits of Charles the First and George the Fourth. A detailed drawing was reproduced, carefully shaded, to show that the very hairs of his head were all numbered. No uninformed person looking at its carefully lined face and wistful eyes would imagine for a moment that this was the portrait of a thigh-bone; or of a few teeth and a fragment of a cranium.[25]

When the first edition of this book, *What About Origins?*, was published in the mid-1970s, it was fairly easy to summarize and criticize evolutionists' views of the origin of humans. Basically, they believed that the australopithecines evolved into *Homo habilis* (the habilines), then into *Homo erectus*, and then into the various members of the *Homo sapiens* family. It was easy to show that this proposed origin of humans was simply not true. Some thirty years later, the proposed evolutionary family tree is still very similar but is more complicated, because it now contains a lot more species and is full of side branches and dead ends. It would take a whole book just to deal with this proposed family tree in detail. I intend, therefore, to give here only the briefest outline and criticism of this family tree.

Australopithecus (meaning 'southern ape') is the name given to a number of different fossils found mostly in East Africa. Many species of australopithecines are known to have existed in the past and they all have strange-sounding names. These names, however, can often tell us where the fossilized remains were first found—for example, *Australopithecus afarensis* tells us that this australopithecine was found in the Afar region of Ethiopia. Sometimes, however, the name will reflect a particular characteristic of the australopithecine: *Australopithecus robustus*, for example, tells us that this australopithecine was robust—strong and sturdy. The australopithecines have a number of species, including *Australopithecus anamensis*, *Australopithecus afarensis*, *Australopithecus africanus*, *Australopithecus garhi*, *Australopithecus aethiopicus*, *Australopithecus robustus*, and *Australopithecus boisei*.

The australopithecines were about 1.2 to 1.5 metres tall, with the male being up to 50 per cent larger than the female. Although evolutionists maintain that the australopithecines were bipedal—that is, upright-walking—the evidence suggests that their mode of locomotion was unique and was probably more similar to that of the orang-utan than to that of any other living creature. Their brains were small and ape-like, with an average capacity of about 450 cc in the gracile varieties (e.g. *Australopithecus africanus*) and about 600 cc in the robust ones (e.g. *Australopithecus robustus*). The australopithecines therefore had brains that were less than half the size of those of modern humans, who have an average brain size of 1350 cc. As already mentioned, the name *Australopithecus* actually means 'southern ape', and this reflects exactly what the australopithecines were—apes. These apes are now extinct and have no ancestral relationship either to humans or to any other extinct or living ape.

Before we leave the australopithecines, we must meet the most famous of them all—Lucy. Lucy was the name given to some bones from an *Australopithecus afarensis*—she was named after the Beatles' song *Lucy in the Sky with Diamonds*, the song that her discoverers were playing on their cassette recorder when they were looking at the bones on the evening of their discovery in 1974. She was discovered near Hadar in the Afar Triangle in Ethiopia by Professor Don Johanson and his colleagues. Only about 40 per cent of the skeleton was found but from this, Johanson estimated her height at just over one metre and her brain size as 380 to 450 cc. Other specimens of *Australopithecus afarensis* have been found, and anthropologists maintain that Lucy and her fellow creatures walked upright just as humans do, although they were essentially ape-like from the neck up. Reconstructions of Lucy show her as an upright-walking creature with a smallish, powerful, human-like body and an ape-like head. It must be remembered, however, that such reconstructions are imaginative rather than factual.

Lucy is always reconstructed as having feet similar to human feet, although if you look carefully at any photograph of the fossilized remains of Lucy's skeleton, you will see that no bones from the feet are present because they were not found. The reason why anthropologists believe that Lucy walked upright is because unmistakably human footprints have been found in Laetoli in Tanzania. These human footprints, along with those of many animals (including hares, antelopes, gazelles, giraffes, elephants, rhinoceroses, pigs, hyenas and baboons) are well-preserved because the humans and the animals walked across a flat area where a layer of volcanic ash had recently been moistened by rain. The moist volcanic ash behaved like concrete: when it dried out, it became rock-hard and effectively preserved the footprints in stone. Evolutionists maintain that these footprints could not possibly have been made by humans—even though they look for all the world like ordinary human footprints that were made by a man and a woman—because humans had apparently not evolved when these footprints were made! The evolutionists therefore conclude that the ape-like australopithecines must have had human-like feet. It is interesting to note how the evolutionists reinterpret this footprint evidence to make it fit their evolutionary views, while the evidence fits perfectly with the biblical view without any reinterpretation necessary whatsoever.

Evolutionists inform us that the australopithecines are our ancestors, and this is subtly imprinted on our minds by a number of factors. Often the australopithecines are referred to as being human, as we saw earlier. The name 'Lucy' is given to one of the australopithecines, and she is singled out as being the ancestor of all humans. Her supposed humanness is subtly imprinted on our minds by her human name. Her humanness is then further imprinted on our minds by calling a juvenile australopithecine 'Lucy's Baby', which is often referred to as a child. In addition, Lucy's supposed humanness is reinforced by the reconstructions showing Lucy walking upright, just like humans, and showing her giving her infant a human cuddle (rather than having her infant cling onto her, as infant apes do). Furthermore, drawings and paintings are made that deliberately show whites in the eyes of the *Australopithecus afarensis* species, even though apes do not have whites in their eyes.[26] The humanness of Lucy is further subtly reinforced by referring to her and her mate and any offspring in any reconstructions as the 'First Family'. Such anthropomorphic terms convey the notion of human-like status to Lucy and to other australopithecines, and this has been firmly established in our minds when, in fact, the australopithecines were nothing more than apes.

There is much speculation about what happened to the australopithecines. The one thing that we can be sure about is that they are now extinct. Evolutionists believe that the australopithecines evolved into humans, but herein lies their predicament, for no half-australopithecine/half-human has ever been found. The attempt to understand exactly what creature is represented by the fossils that have been found in Africa is fraught with difficulties, one being the fact that, as we have seen, evolutionists deliberately give names that bestow humanness to the creatures from which the fossils have come, even when those creatures are manifestly nothing but apes.

We find further examples of this when we investigate what evolutionists teach about the origin of humans. One example involves *Paranthropus*, meaning 'beside man'. The fossil remains of this creature actually show it to be similar to an australopithecine but with a slightly broader face, slightly larger chewing teeth, and small incisors and canines. Its brain size is similar to that of *Australopithecus africanus*. No one can tell how the creature walked because no postcranial fossils have been found, so evolutionists can only guess about its posture and locomotion.[27] It appears, then, that 'beside man' is really just a variant australopithecine and has nothing at all to do with the origin of humans.

Another example is *Homo habilis*, a name that means 'handy man'. In 1960, Louis and Mary Leakey made the first of a series of remarkable discoveries of bones that they thought belonged to a creature that was a human-like ape-man. As usual, they did not find a complete skeleton: they found some teeth, part of the top of a cranium, some hand-bones, and most of the left foot. The next year, the Leakeys found the incomplete skull of an adolescent, more cranial-bone fragments, a lower jaw and more teeth. Similar fossils have been found at other sites in East and southern Africa. Even today, scientists are debating whether these remains belonged to the transitional form suggested by the Leakeys or to an australopithecine. One reason for this is that the brain size for this creature ranged from 500 cc to 800 cc—the smaller measurement being similar to that of the australopithecines and the larger being only half the size of that of modern humans. Another reason is that their limb proportions make them indistinguishable from *Australopithecus afarensis*.[28] In fact, there is little to distinguish *Homo habilis* from the australopithecines, despite the human name given to it. In other words, *Homo habilis* is nothing more than an ape!

Humankind, past and present
According to evolutionists, the australopithecines evolved into humans,

but, as we have already noted, there is no proof of this because no half-australopithecine/half-human creature has been found in the fossil record. What has been found, however, are the fossilized remains of a number of different creatures that have all been assigned to the genus *Homo* and which all belong to the human kind. To understand this we must remember what we learned about the variations within kinds—for example, within the wolf–dog kind and within the *Brassica* kind. We shall see that there are a number of variations within the human kind, and it would be fair to say that we can see how one variety of humans has changed into another variety. The variations that we observe in modern humans living on the earth today are not confined to skin colour, but are also reflected in the physical differences that we see in the various races. These physical differences include height, body shape, head shape, nose shape and length, as well as the noses' internal structures. Yet with all these differences, members of the different races of modern humans are capable of interbreeding, because they are all members of the human kind. We must realize, however, that the variations that we find in humans are not the result of evolution; they are just variations within a kind (in this case, the human kind) as taught in the Bible.

One variety of humankind I want us to consider are the *Homo erectus* people. Although there is still discussion about what creatures should and should not be included in this variety of humankind, there are good, sound reasons for believing that some of the fossils that have been designated as being different species of humans (for example, *Homo ergaster*, *Homo heidelbergensis* and Boxgrove Man) should be included. The fossilized remains of *Homo erectus* people have been found in Africa (Kenya and Tanzania), Europe (England, Germany, Georgia, Spain and Turkey) and Asia (India, Indonesia, Vietnam and China).

Members of this variety of humankind walked upright, stood at anywhere up to 1.8 metres tall and were much stronger than modern humans. They had a brain size of up to 1400 cc, although the average was slightly smaller but still well within the variations found in modern humans. They had a crude culture that involved the use of simple implements and weapons for hunting, and there is evidence that they were able to control fire. Perhaps the most amazing thing we know about these

Chapter 9

people is that they made very elegant double-edged, teardrop-shaped 'hand axes'—at least, that is what they are called, although there is no firm agreement about their use. It has been suggested that they could have been cutting and chopping tools, digging implements, flake cores or used in animal traps, or that they had a purely ritual significance (e.g. as part of courting behaviour). The current majority scientific view, however, is that they were tools for some form of chopping or for general-purpose use, probably for cutting meat and extracting bone marrow (which would explain their pointed ends) and general hacking through bone and muscle fibre. The manufacture of these hand axes, however, indicates that these people used their brains in a similar way to how we use our brains today, as they had the ability to conceive a design for a stone tool and then to work a piece of flint until that design was achieved. This is known as 'conceptualized thinking'; according to linguists, this is the type of thinking that we do when we speak a language. The manufacture of these hand axes therefore provides good evidence that the *Homo erectus* people were able to speak to one another. There is no reason for us to think that the *Homo erectus* people were anything other than fully human.

The other variety of humankind I want us to consider is *Homo sapiens*. There are two varieties of humans within *Homo sapiens*. One of these is the Neanderthal people, which we have already discussed. As we have already noted, there is discussion as to whether the Neanderthals should be a separate species—*Homo neanderthalensis*—or whether they should be put into a sub-species of *Homo sapiens*—in which case they would be designated *Homo sapiens neanderthalensis*. If they were designated as a sub-species of *Homo sapiens*, the other sub-species, or variety, of *Homo sapiens* would be the modern human, who would then be designated *Homo sapiens sapiens*.

Bernard Wood is Professor of Human Origins at George Washington University and Adjunct Senior Scientist in the Human Origins Programme at the National Museum of Natural History, the Smithsonian Institution. He is an evolutionist and has written extensively about human origins,[29] yet, in an article published in *New Scientist*, he wrote the following concerning the well-known illustration of the supposed evolution of apes through ape-like transitions to humans:

There is a popular image of human evolution that you'll find all over the place … On the left of the picture there's an ape … On the right, a man … Between the two is a succession of figures that become ever more like humans … Our progress from ape to human looks so smooth, so tidy. It's such a beguiling image that even the experts are loath to let it go. But it is an illusion.[30]

One of the world's leading experts on human origins tells us that the popular image of human evolution that we see all over the place—the one showing the gradual smooth change from apes to three-quarter ape/one-quarter human, to half-ape/half-human, to three-quarter-human/one-quarter ape, to human—is *an illusion*! Actually, what we have seen in this chapter confirms that what Professor Wood said is correct. Evolutionists have found apes in the fossil record, and they have found humans. But they have still not found the elusive so-called missing links, for the simple reason that they are missing. This means that evolutionists still cannot use the fossil record to give us an evolutionary account of the origin of humans. This is exactly what we would expect, given the biblical account of creation and early history of the earth.

Some people think that, if we accept what the Bible teaches about origins, there is a problem with the number of people that we find living on the earth in the twenty-first century. If we accept what the Bible teaches about there being only one human pair just a few thousand years ago, is it possible to reach the present human population on the earth in this short period of time? This question can be answered by constructing a population clock. Let us start with a single human pair—a man and a woman. Let them marry and have children, and let their children marry and have children and so on. Let us assume that the population doubles every 150 years—a very conservative figure, as the world human population doubled in the forty-year period between 1960 and 2000, from three billion to six billion.[31] Our conservative figure allows for the population growth to be disrupted by famines, diseases, wars and natural disasters.

Starting with just two people, then, after 150 years there will be four people; after another 150 years there will be eight people; after another 150 years there will be sixteen people and so on. After thirty-three doublings, the world population will have reached almost 8.5 billion people—that's a couple of billion more than the estimated population of the earth in 2000. Now, thirty-three doublings would take place in only 4,950 years—not the millions of years that one might think would be necessary to reach the world's present population. As one would expect, this figure is perfectly consistent with the biblical teaching that the creation of humans took place just a few thousand years ago. Such a conservative population clock also shows that humans could not possibly have been living on the earth for even tens of thousands of years, because within around 10,000 years there would be more people on the earth than the number of atoms in the universe. While I am fully aware that such a situation could not possibly occur, I simply use it to demonstrate that this simple conservative population clock demonstrates that humans could not have been around on the earth for anywhere near the time that evolutionists maintain. This is yet another nail in the coffin of human evolution.

Atheism and evolution

It is my experience that many people just cannot accept that evolution is a religion. Many will claim that Darwinism is a religion, but will argue that evolution is not a religion but scientific fact. This is strange, because many of the proponents of evolution argue that evolution *is* a religion. Dr Michael Ruse serves as Lucyle T. Werkmeister Professor of Philosophy at Florida State University. He is a philosopher of science and has written several books on evolutionary theory. In an article in the *National Post*, he wrote, 'Evolution is promoted by its practitioners as more than mere science. Evolution is promulgated as an ideology, a secular religion—a full-fledged alternative to Christianity, with meaning and morality … Evolution is a religion. This was true of evolution in the beginning, and it is true of evolution still today.'[32]

Although the admission that evolution is more than 'mere science' and that it is a 'secular religion' is barely credible, it is to be expected. Professor Phillip E. Johnson is emeritus Professor of Law at Boalt School of Law at University of California, Berkeley. He has criticized evolution from the basis of his legal expertise, which is the evidence of evidence. In an interview in August 2003, he argued that 'The whole point of Darwinism is to show that there is no need for a supernatural Creator, because nature can do the creating by itself'.[33] In other words, Professor Johnson argues that, because evolution can account for the origin of *everything*, believing in evolution negates the need for believing in a Creator. In a bizarre twist, some evolutionists have argued that, during the evolution of humans, their brains evolved a belief in a supernatural god, so they argue that the Creator God of the Bible is a product of evolution! Is there no end to the depraved arguments that atheistic evolutionists will utilize in order to make an excuse for their not believing in God?

Other influential evolutionists have similar views to those quoted above from Dr Michael Ruse. For example, in a debate with Professor Philip E. Johnson at Stanford University on 30 April 1994, William Provine, a professor in the Department of Ecology and Evolutionary Biology at Cornell University, said to his debating opponent and to the audience, 'Let me summarize my views on what modern evolutionary biology tells us loud and clear—and these are basically Darwin's views …' When I read this, I expected this respected evolutionary scientist to share his understanding about the origin of life, or something insightful about natural selection, or something profound about the origin of species. But what he said next was incredible; he enlightened his audience by telling them that evolutionary biology tells us loud and clear that 'There are no gods, no purposes, no goal-directed forces of any kind. There is no life after death. When I die, I am absolutely certain that I am going to be dead. That's the end of me. There is no ultimate foundation for ethics, no ultimate meaning in life, and no free will for humans, either.'[34]

It is obvious, therefore, that evolution is the theology of atheism. As we have seen above, according to its proponents evolution does not need any supernatural agent (that is, God) to make it work, and evolution, through natural processes, is responsible for everything. As a result, many people have been led to atheism because of the theory of evolution—one of these being the famous atheist Professor Richard Dawkins. He made this crystal clear in an interview given in 2005 when, in answer to the question 'Is atheism the logical extension of believing in evolution?' he responded by saying, 'My personal feeling is that understanding evolution led *me* to atheism' (his emphasis).[35] This is why the subject of origins is so important; belief in evolution has prevented many from trusting in the Creator God that we read about in the Bible.

The idea that evolution leads to atheism was aptly demonstrated by Professor William Provine, when he wrote that '... belief in modern evolution makes atheists of people. One can have a religious view that is compatible with evolution only if the religious view is indistinguishable from atheism.'[36]

There is no doubt that modern evolutionists are, in general, Darwinian fundamentalists who actively, and sometimes aggressively, promote their atheistic belief system. Their belief system has been accurately summed up with great understanding by the Roman Catholic journalist Paul Johnson as follows: 'Nature does not distinguish between a range of mountains, like the Alps, or a stone, or a clever scientist like Professor Dawkins, because it is sightless, senseless and mindless, being a mere process operating according to rules which have not been designed but simply are.'[37] Paul Johnson is actually referring to evolution when he uses the word 'nature', for he is referring to the supposed chance natural processes that were then sorted by natural selection over the eons in which the evolutionists believe. Evolutionists believe that *everything* has come about as a result of evolution. According to them, evolutionary processes are completely blind—there is no purpose to them, and the universe and everything in it, including me and you, just happen to be products of these processes. Evolution therefore teaches that there is no purpose to our existence. We just happen to be, and our only purpose is to pass on our genes to the next generation of humans. According to evolutionists, me, you, every plant and animal, the earth, the sun, the moon and all the stars in the universe, as well as the space–time continuum of the universe, are all the result, not of a powerful, supernatural Creator God, but of an initial explosion of nothing and its subsequent evolution.

Having established that evolution is a religion, it is now possible to compare and contrast the false religion of evolution with the true religion of Christianity. This will explain more fully why evolution is a religion and why so many people find it emotionally and religiously fulfilling to embrace it. The six tenets of evolution that can be compared and contrasted with Christianity are as follows:[38]

- *A holy book.* Christianity has the Bible, which is the inspired Word of God. Evolution has Darwin's *On the Origin of Species*.[39]
- *An explanation for the origin of everything.* Christianity has creation by an all-powerful God. Evolution has chance natural processes honed by natural selection.
- *An explanation for death and suffering.* Christianity has death and suffering being introduced into the perfect world created by Almighty God as a result of the first man's sin. Evolution does not recognize sin but teaches that the evolution of lifeless molecules to living humans can only proceed via the survival of the fittest; death and suffering are thus the necessary driving forces of evolution.
- *The reason why we are here.* Christianity teaches that humans are the pinnacle of God's creation and that we are made in God's image and likeness and are to enjoy him for ever. Evolution teaches that we are just here—the product of the evolution of life—and that our purpose is to pass on our genes to the next generation.
- *Our future.* Christianity teaches that one day the Lord Jesus Christ will return to this earth and that God will create new heavens and a new earth, where those who in this life trusted Jesus as their Lord and Saviour will live with God for ever. Evolution, on the other hand, teaches that humans are not the end-product of evolution and that evolution will continue, with the result that humans will either become extinct or will evolve into another kind of creature.
- *The future of the universe.* Christianity teaches that the present universe will be burned up by God and that he will then create new heavens and a new earth. Evolution, as we saw in Chapter 6, teaches a far more depressing future, with the universe experiencing what is called a 'heat death' (although in reality it should be called a 'cold death', for the temperature of the universe will be just a fraction of a degree above absolute zero).

In Chapter 7, I related the story of the research worker who had a Ph.D. in Biology and who preferred to believe that carbon atoms had desires and feelings rather than believe in a God who would be 'telling him what to do in his life'. It is this aspect of Christianity—God telling us what to do—that makes many turn away from God and enjoy what the Bible calls 'the pleasures of sin for a season' (Heb. 11:25, KJV). These adherents to the religion of evolution are not slow to admit this, as is borne out by the following quote:

We no longer feel ourselves to be guests in someone else's home and therefore obliged to make our behavior conform with a set of pre-existing cosmic rules. It is our creation now. *We make the rules.* We establish the parameters of reality. We create the world, and because we do, we no longer feel beholden to outside forces. We no longer have to justify our behaviour, for we are now the architects of the universe. We are responsible to nothing outside ourselves, for we are the kingdom, the power, and the glory for ever and ever [emphasis added].[40]

Evolution gives people an excuse to do as they please because, for them, there is no God to whom they have to give an account of their life and of the actions and decisions they have made while living that life. This has resulted in the present hedonistic society in which we find ourselves living—a society in which people endeavour to live for pleasure, eating and drinking with no thought that perhaps tomorrow they will die. Unless they are saved beforehand, it will only be when they do die that they will know the truth—that it is appointed unto us all to die, and after that will come the judgement, when we will all have to stand before the Almighty and give account of ourselves to him.

Conclusion

In this chapter we have seen that there is no evidence for the proposed evolutionary origin of humans. We have seen that the history of the evolutionists' quest for the story of the evolution of humans is littered with mistakes and frauds. We have seen that illustrations depicting ape-people are the products of the imaginations of the artists who drew them. Fossil ape-people have never been found because they have never existed. Humans are not the product of evolution; we are all descended from Adam and Eve, the first human pair, who were created by God.

Yet, despite this, the evolutionary view of the history of humankind still dominates our philosophy. So-called 'early humans' are thought to have been primitive intellectually, culturally, technologically, as well as physically and spiritually. The story of humankind is thought to be a steady upward advance in all these spheres. The Bible, however, paints a very different picture of the history of humankind. Instead of developing from a half-ape/half-human creature, the first pair of our ancestors were, according to the Bible, part of God's perfect creation—creatures made in the image of God and who were morally, intellectually, physically and spiritually perfect. Instead of gradually evolving upwards, humans, as presented in the Bible, are fallen beings who have sinned against their Creator and are morally, intellectually and physically degenerate and spiritually destitute, alienated from God. This sorry state in which we find ourselves is the result of sin—in particular, Adam's sin.

The Bible refutes the evolutionary concept of the progressive improvement of humankind, and teaches that there is only one way back to God—in and through his Son, the Lord Jesus Christ. The apostle Paul, in his first letter to the church at Corinth, contrasted the inheritance which we have through Adam's sin with that which we can receive in Christ. For instance, in Adam we inherit death, but in Christ we can be made alive (1 Cor. 15:22). In Adam, we live lives fulfilling the works of the flesh ('adultery, fornication, uncleanness, lewdness, idolatry, sorcery, hatred, contentions, jealousies, outbursts of wrath, selfish ambitions, dissensions, heresies, envy, murders, drunkenness, revelries, and the like'—Gal. 5:19–21), the *wages* of which is death (Rom. 6:23). In Christ, we can know a life bearing the fruit of the Spirit ('love, joy, peace, longsuffering, kindness, goodness, faithfulness, gentleness, self-control'—Gal. 5:22–23) and we can have eternal life, the *gift* of God (Rom. 6:23).

Notes

1 From personal observation.

2 See, for example, **Bernard Wood,** *Human Evolution: A Very Short Introduction* (Oxford: Oxford University Press, 2005).

3 The Neander Valley is named after the famous German Christian and hymn-writer Joachim Neander, who lived from 1650 to 1680. He used to visit a cave in this valley and there write hymns. One of Neander's hymns translated from German into English by Catherine Winkworth begins, 'Praise to the Lord, the Almighty, the King of creation!'

4 'Neanderthal of the North Sea', Natural History Museum, 15 June 2009, at: nhm.ac.uk.

5 **John Noble Wilford,** 'Discovery Suggests Humans Are a Bit Neanderthal', 25 April 1999, at: cogweb.ucla.edu/ep/Neanderthal.html.

6 **Ian Sample,** 'Scientists Unravel Neanderthal Genome', 12 February 2009, at: guardian.co.uk.

7 **A. J. E. Cave** and **W. L. Straus Jr,** 'Pathology and Posture of Neanderthal Man', in *Quarterly Review of Biology,* vol. 32 (1957), pp. 348–363.

8 Quoted by **Will Dunham,** 'Neanderthals Trekked All the Way into Siberia' 1 October 2007, at: reuters.com.

9 **Irene White,** 'Kinver Caveman', in *Answers,* 2/1 (January–March 2007), pp. 38–39.

10 An examination of the Neanderthals' genome shows that many of them had red hair. See **Paul Rincon,** 'Neanderthals "Were Flame-Haired"', 25 October 2007, at: news.bbc.co.uk.

11 See under 'Business of the House', 26 November 1953, at: hansard.millbanksystems.com. The full motion was 'That this House has no confidence in the trustees of the British Museum, other than the Speaker of the House of Commons, because of the tardiness of their discovery that the skull of the Piltdown Man is a partial fake.'

12 **William K. Gregory,** '*Hesperopithecus* Apparently Not an Ape Nor a Man', in *Science,* vol. 66 (1927), pp. 579–581.

13 'First Glimpse of a Stone-Age Tribe', in *National Geographic Magazine,* vol. 140 (December 1971), pp. 881–882.

14 *Scandal of the Lost Tribe,* first broadcast in the UK on 23 August 1988 (ITV).

15 'Hominid Collarbone Exposed as Dolphin's Rib', in *New Scientist* (28 April 1983), p. 199.

16 'Ass is Taken for a Man', in *The Daily Telegraph,* 14 May 1984, p. 16.

17 **Tim D. White, Gen Suwa** and **Berhane Asfaw,** '*Australopithecus ramidus,* a New Species of Early Hominid from Aramis, Ethiopia', in *Nature,* 371 (1994), pp. 306–312.

18 **Tim D. White,** Gen Suwa and Berhane Asfaw, '*Ardipithecus ramidus,* a New Species of Early Hominid from Aramis, Ethiopia', in *Nature,* 375 (1995), p. 88.

19 **James Owen,** '"Lucy's Baby"—World's Oldest Child—Found by Fossil Hunters', 20 September 2006, at: nationalgeographic.com.

20 **Alemseged Zeresenay et al.,** 'A Juvenile Early Hominin Skeleton from Dikika, Ethiopia', in *Nature,* 443 (21 September 2006), pp. 296–301.

21 '"Lucy's Baby" Found in Ethiopia', 20 September 2006, at: news.bbc.co.uk.

22 **Brad Harrub,** 'Lucy's Baby?' (2006), at: apologeticspress.org.

23 **Bernard Wood,** 'A Precious Little Bundle', in *Nature,* 443 (21 September 2006), pp. 278–281.

24 **Russell L. Ciochon,** 'The Mystery Ape of Pleistocene Asia', in *Nature*, 459 (18 June 2009), pp. 910–911.

25 **G. K. Chesterton,** *The Everlasting Man* (EasyRead Comfort Edition, 2006), p. 25, at: books.google.co.uk.

26 **John Gurche,** an American artist and sculptor, stated in an article in *National Geographic Magazine* that he painted whites in the eyes of an *Australopithecus afarensis* as he wanted to get a human soul into this ape-like face to indicate something about its destiny (*National Geographic Magazine*, 189/3 (March 1996), pp. 96–117).

27 **Wood,** *Human Evolution: A Very Short Introduction*, p. 78.

28 Ibid. p. 81.

29 See, for example, **Wood,** *Human Evolution: A Very Short Introduction*.

30 **Bernard Wood,** 'Who Are We?', in *New Scientist*, no. 2366 (26 October 2002), p. 44.

31 US Census Bureau, International Data Base (December 2008 Update).

32 **Michael Ruse,** 'Saving Darwinism from the Darwinians', in *National Post* (13 May 2000), p. B-3.

33 From an interview in *WORLD Magazine*, reprinted in *Evangelicals Now* (August 2003).

34 'Darwinism: Science or Natural Philosophy?', in *Origins Research*, 16/1 (1994); also at: arn.org.

35 **Laura Sheahen** and **Dr Richard Dawkins,** 'The Problem with God: Interview with Richard Dawkins', 11 November 2005, at: beliefnet.com/News/Science-Religion/2005/11/The-Problem-With-God-Interview-With-Richard-Dawkins.aspx.

36 **William Provine,** 'No Free Will', in **Margaret W. Rossiter,** (ed.), *Catching up with the Vision* (Chicago: Chicago University Press, 1999), p. S123.

37 **Paul Johnson,** 'Where the Darwinian Fundamentalists are Leading Us', in *The Spectator*, 23 April 2005, p. 32.

38 This comparison follows closely that given in **A. J. Monty White** and **Dr Tommy Mitchell,** 'Is Evolution a Religion?' in **Ken Ham,** (ed.), *The New Answers Book 2* (Green Forest, AR: Master Books, 2008), pp. 207–217.

39 A Professor of Biology once told me that he believed Darwin's writings to be inspired, and that he read from *On the Origin of Species* for at least twenty minutes every night before retiring to bed.

40 **Jeremy Rifkin,** *Algeny* (New York: Viking, 1983), p. 244.

General conclusion

The title of his book is set in the form of a question: 'What about origins?' As we have seen, this question can be answered with another: 'Evolution or creation?' And as we have also seen, these two accounts of origins are irreconcilable: one account attempts to explain origins naturalistically; the other account is supernatural.

Evolution teaches that there are no reasons for the existence of the universe, the solar system, the earth, the myriad life forms on earth or humans. This is reflected in the teachings and writings of atheists when they talk about living in a universe that has no design or purpose, and where there is no evil and no good—nothing but blind, pitiless indifference. The story of evolution is totally directionless and is without purpose, serving only to ensure the survival of the fittest. According to evolution, the universe is the result of 'nothing' exploding. Life on earth is the result of inorganic compounds linking up to form complex organic molecules that were capable of reproducing themselves without the intervention of any intelligent designer. Humans are here because an odd group of fish had a peculiar fin anatomy that evolved into limbs so that terrestrial animals could evolve, and because of a huge meteor that struck the earth, wiping out the dinosaurs, thus giving mammals a chance to evolve that would not otherwise have been available. According to evolution, humans are not the pinnacle of evolution, because evolution will continue; as a result, humans will either become extinct as they fail to evolve, or they will evolve into a new kind of creature that will definitely not be human.

Creation, on the other hand, can be summed up in one verse of Scripture: 'For in six days the LORD made the heavens and the earth, the sea, and all that is in them, and rested the seventh day' (Exod. 20:11). Creation also teaches why God created—he did so for his own pleasure: 'Thou art worthy, O Lord, to receive glory and honour and power: for thou hast created all things, and for thy pleasure they are and were created' (Rev. 4:11, KJV).

Creation teaches that there is a purpose for the universe. It was created so that it would declare the glory of God: 'The heavens declare the glory of God; and the firmament [the expanse of heaven] shows His handiwork' (Ps. 19:1). Creation teaches that there is a purpose for the earth—God created it so that it could support life, so that it could be inhabited by humans: 'For thus saith the LORD that created the heavens; God himself that formed the earth and made it; he hath established it, he created it not in vain, he formed it to be inhabited: I am the LORD; and there is none else' (Isa. 45:18, KJV). Creation teaches that there is a purpose for humans—to have dominion over God's creation: 'Then God said, "Let Us make man in Our image, according to Our likeness; let them have dominion over the fish of the sea, over the birds of the air, and over the cattle, over all the earth and over every creeping thing that creeps on the earth"' (Gen. 1:26).

Finally, the reason for our existence is given in the Westminster Catechism, when, in response to the question about what is the chief and highest end of humankind, the answer is given that we should glorify God and enjoy him for ever. This should be the focus of our desire—to glorify and enjoy our Creator for ever and ever.

About Day One:

Day One's threefold commitment:

- TO BE FAITHFUL TO THE BIBLE, GOD'S INERRANT, INFALLIBLE WORD;

- TO BE RELEVANT TO OUR MODERN GENERATION;

- TO BE EXCELLENT IN OUR PUBLICATION STANDARDS.

I continue to be thankful for the publications of Day One. They are biblical; they have sound theology; and they are relative to the issues at hand. The material is condensed and manageable while, at the same time, being complete—a challenging balance to find. We are happy in our ministry to make use of these excellent publications.

JOHN MACARTHUR, PASTOR-TEACHER, GRACE COMMUNITY CHURCH, CALIFORNIA

It is a great encouragement to see Day One making such excellent progress. Their publications are always biblical, accessible and attractively produced, with no compromise on quality. Long may their progress continue and increase!

JOHN BLANCHARD, AUTHOR, EVANGELIST AND APOLOGIST

Visit our website for more information and to request a free catalogue of our books.

www.dayone.co.uk

Evolution: good science?
Exposing the ideological
nature of Darwin's theory

DOMINIC STATHAM

160PP, ILLUSTRATED PAPERBACK

978-1-84625-170-2

**Evolution:
Good Science?**
Exposing the ideological nature
of Darwin's theory

Dominic Statham   DayOne

Darwin's theory of evolution is often presented as scientifically proven fact. Few are aware, however, that there are serious problems with the theory. We are only told about the evidence that appears to support it, yet many scientific observations seriously undermine it.

Using plain English, Dominic Statham explains the main arguments presented by evolutionists and reveals their major flaws. He shows that much of the scientific data is actually consistent with a biblical account of creation and gives readers confidence to hold fast to the Bible as the true revelation of God, his creation and his dealings with mankind.

'... an excellent summary of the origins debate. Dominic Statham is well qualified to take on the task of analysing a mass of disputed evidence and making conclusions that are fair and justified.'
STUART BURGESS, PROFESSOR OF DESIGN AND NATURE, UNIVERSITY OF BRISTOL

'I enjoyed this book very much! I recommend it to anyone interested in the origins controversy.'
DR R. TERRY SPOHN, PROFESSOR OF BIOLOGY AND ASSOCIATE DIRECTOR OF CREATION STUDIES, LIBERTY UNIVERSITY, LYNCHBURG, VIRGINIA, USA

Dominic Statham is a chartered engineer and graduate of Loughborough University. He has twenty-five years' experience in aeronautical and automotive engineering, with Rolls Royce (Aero and Industrial & Marine Divisions) and GKN, a leading supplier of automotive driveline components. His recent vehicle projects include Land Rover Discovery 3, Freelander 2 and the Jaguar XF. He has extensive experience of both manufacturing and product development, and holds a number of patents.

Hallmarks of design:
Evidence of design in the natural world

STUART BURGESS

256PP, ILLUSTRATED PAPERBACK

ISBN 978–1–846251–39–9

The Design Argument contends that design in nature reveals a Designer. *Hallmarks of Design* presents this in the light of the latest discoveries about the complexity and beauty of the natural world. Features of the book include:

- Six clear hallmarks of design;
- Over thirty diagrams;
- Description of how the earth is designed for mankind;
- Description of the Creator's attributes

Dr Stuart Burgess is Head of Department of Mechanical Engineering at the University of Bristol. His research areas include the study of design in nature. He previously worked in industry, designing rocket and satellite systems for the European Space Agency. He is winner of the Worshipful Company of Turners Gold Medal for the design of the solar array deployment system on the £1·4 billion ENVISAT earth observation satellite.

'Compelling presentation of the evidence of design in the natural world.'
—*BANNER OF TRUTH MAGAZINE*

He made the stars also:
What the Bible says about the stars

STUART BURGESS

192PP, ILLUSTRATED PAPERBACK

ISBN 978–1–846251–20–7

This book teaches clearly and biblically the purpose of the stars and the question of extra-terrestrial life. Dr Burgess explains how the earth has a unique purpose in supporting life and how the stars have a singular purpose in shining light on it. He explains why the universe contains such natural beauty and how the stars reveal God's character.

Dr Stuart Burgess is Head of Department of Mechanical Engineering at the University of Bristol. His research areas include the study of design in nature. He previously worked in industry, designing rocket and satellite systems for the European Space Agency. He is winner of the Worshipful Company of Turners Gold Medal for the design of the solar array deployment system on the £1·4 billion ENVISAT earth observation satellite.

'Dr Burgess has a very clear style and his book brims with interesting material. It will be greatly appreciated.'
—DR PETER MASTERS, METROPOLITAN TABERNACLE

'Both our world and the heavens seem to sparkle with a new identity as a consequence of this book.'
GEOFF THOMAS

'There is a great need for a book which gives clear biblical teaching on the purpose of the stars and the question of extra-terrestrial life. This book meets that need.'
CREATION SCIENCE MOVEMENT

The origin of man
The image of God or
The image of an ape

STUART BURGESS

192 PP PAPERBACK

ISBN 978–1–903087–73–2

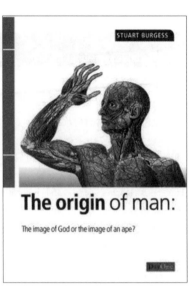

The origin of man:

The image of God or the image of an ape?

Have humans descended from apes or was man specially created? Do humans have unique characteristics and abilities that set them apart from all the animals? The answers to these crucial questions determine whether man is just an animal or a special spiritual being. This book shows that there is overwhelming evidence that man has a Creator. The book has many diagrams and includes explanation of similarities between humans and apes, unique characteristics of humans, unique beauty of humans, archaeological and fossil evidence and the importance and relevance of the origins debate.

Dr Stuart Burgess, BSc, PhD, CEng, MIMechE, is a Reader in Engineering Design at Bristol University. His research areas include the study of design in nature. He previously worked in industry, designing rocket and satellite systems for the European Space Agency. He is winner of the Worshipful Company of Turners Gold Medal for the design of the solar array deployment system on the £1.4 billion ENVISAT earth observation satellite.

PHILIP SNOW

240PP ILLUSTRATED PAPERBACK

ISBN 978–1–846250–02–6

Birds are amongst the world's most beautiful and beloved creations, so it is unsurprising that they have been so widely studied. This book examines closely their wonderful aerial lifestyle and unique, warm-blooded design—often so different from the cold-blooded dinosaurs that they are claimed to have accidentally 'evolved' from! Especially as they often precede dinosaurs in the fossil record and their miraculous genetics, as ours, speaks of special Creation—not random 'Big Bangs', chance chemical soups and endless genetic mistakes! They have been carved and painted since earliest times, on rocks, temples and associated with pyramids and religions, art and literature, sport and farming, war and peace and even Heaven and Hell.

Philip Snow is a wildlife and landscape painter, illustrator and writer. His work appears in many publications and galleries and he has illustrated, or contributed work to, over sixty books and many magazines, prints, cards, calendars, reserve guides and decorated maps etc. Publications include several Collins guides to UK and European birds, and paintings have been exhibited in many top galleries, in the UK and abroad. Latest books (2005) include a Hebridean Wildlife and Landscape Sketchbook, several Children's Biblical colouring books, a book on estuary life and migration and regularly exhibitions of paintings and prints.

'Philip Snow has produced a unique book which expertly describes and illustrates the design, life and beauty of birds.'
STUART C BURGESS, PROFESSOR OF DESIGN AND NATURE, UNIVERSITY OF BRISTOL

In God's image
The divine origins of humans

STUART BURGESS

32 PP.

ISBN 978-1-84625-100-9

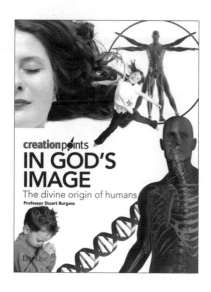

Humans have great physical, mental and spiritual abilities that are far beyond what is needed for survival. This 'over-design' provides compelling evidence that man was specially created as a spiritual being. This booklet describes the following unique characteristics of humans:

- Unique upright structure
- Unique skilful hands
- Unique fine skin
- Unique facial expressions
- Unique language and speech
- Unique childhood
- Unique marriage and birth
- Unique brain
- Unique beauty
- Unique genome
- Unique spirituality

The booklet also discusses the origin of man and the purpose of human life from a biblical perspective.

Stuart Burgess has taught engineering design at leading UK universities. He has also carried out spacecraft design for the European Space Agency. In 1989 he received a Design Council Prize for engineering design presented by the Minister of State for Trade and Industry. In 1993 he received the Turners Gold Medal for engineering design presented by the Vice Chancellor of City University.

Creation & Evolution
Why it matters what you believe

COLIN GARNER

32 PP.

ISBN 978–1–84625–099–6

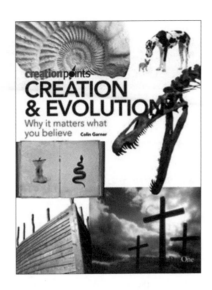

Why is the creation/evolution issue so important? And hasn't science disproved the biblical creation account anyway? The world's evolutionary view permeates virtually all society and secular science, and many people, even Christians, hold an evolutionary view almost by default. They reject the biblical creation account in Genesis as fact. In this booklet Colin Garner demonstrates that, as well as being inconsistent with biblical truth, evolutionary theory has serious fundamental scientific weaknesses. He highlights the reasons why Genesis, the first book of the Bible, is of such foundational importance to life today, in the hope that it will encourage us all to base our beliefs, our evangelism and our hopes on the whole Bible, including its vital foundational teaching on creation.

Colin Garner PhD is professor of applied thermodynamics at a leading UK university. He conducts research for the UK Government and several major international engine, vehicle and fuel companies. His research has been featured in *New Scientist* and he has presented his work on national BBC TV and radio. He lecturers on creation/evolution at the East Midlands School of Christian Ministry. Colin is married to Sue and they have three children.

Genesis for today
The relevance of the creation/
evolution debate to today's society

ANDY MCINTOSH

240PP ILLUSTRATED PAPERBACK

ISBN 978–1–84625–051–4

Professor McIntosh is a scientist who sees no contradiction between science and the events of creation in the book of Genesis. He believes that all Christian doctrine, directly or indirectly, has its basis in the literal events of the first eleven chapters of the Bible, and that these foundations of the faith are being undermined in the church by the fallible theories of evolution.

'For those who have eyes to see, here is ample proof that God's revealed truth is as trustworthy as ever—and infinitely more certain than every human speculation.'
—*JOHN MACARTHUR*

Andy McIntosh, DSc, FIMA, CMath, FEI, CEng, FInstP, MIGEM, FRAeS, is Professor of Thermodynamics and Combustion Theory at the University of Leeds. He has had a career spanning thirty years of conducting scientific research in mathematics, combustion and aeronautics, both in academia and government establishments. He is married with three children and speaks regularly in the UK and abroad concerning the importance of origins. Latterly, his research has

Genesis for today
Showing the relevance of the Creation/Evolution debate to today's society
'Genesis **IS** for today'—JOHN MACARTHUR

THIRD EDITION

WITH NEW CHAPTER: 'GENESIS AND THE 21ST CENTURY'

Day One

brought in the life sciences, with the study of the bombardier beetle, and the whole field of biomimetics—learning engineering solutions from nature.

Darwin and Darwinism 150 years on
Biblical faith and the Christian worldview

IAN MCNAUGHTON AND PAUL TAYLOR

112PP ILLUSTRATED PAPERBACK

ISBN 978–1–84625–162–7

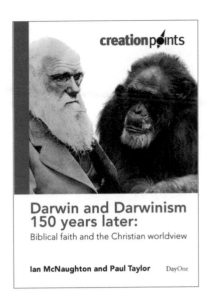

creationpoints

Darwin and Darwinism 150 years later:
Biblical faith and the Christian worldview

Ian McNaughton and Paul Taylor   DayOne

In 1859 Charles Robert Darwin published *On the Origin of Species*, a book that has had a profound impact on the Western world ever since. Why was this book and its ideas so popular? There can be no reason other than that the UK public were ready to embrace an alternative to the biblical creation account. Here Ian McNaughton and Paul Taylor review Charles Darwin's religious ideas, setting them in the context of his background and family, and examine his evolutionary claims in the light of the Bible, which sets forth a worldview consistent with faith in God.

'My colleagues Ian and Paul share my burden to reach Darwin's homeland with the life-changing creation/gospel message. May God bless their effort to show Britons—and others who read this book—that God's Word is accurate and authoritative in our modern-day society.'
KEN HAM, PRESIDENT, ANSWERS IN GENESIS/CREATION MUSEUM, USA

'This excellent book … explains how theistic evolution is not a reconciliation of science with the Bible but rather a damaging union of humanism and the Bible.'
PROFESSOR STUART BURGESS, PROFESSOR OF DESIGN AND NATURE, UK, AND AUTHOR OF HALLMARKS OF DESIGN

Ian McNaughton is Chairman of Answers in Genesis (UK/Europe). He has degrees in Theology and Historical Theology, and is Pastor of West Worthing Evangelical Church, UK. Paul Taylor is the Senior Speaker with Answers in Genesis (UK). He spent seventeen years teaching science and has a Masters degree in Science Education. He is the author of *The Six Days of Genesis, Truth, Lies and Science Education* and *In the Beginning*.